Junior Certificate Civic, Social and Political Education

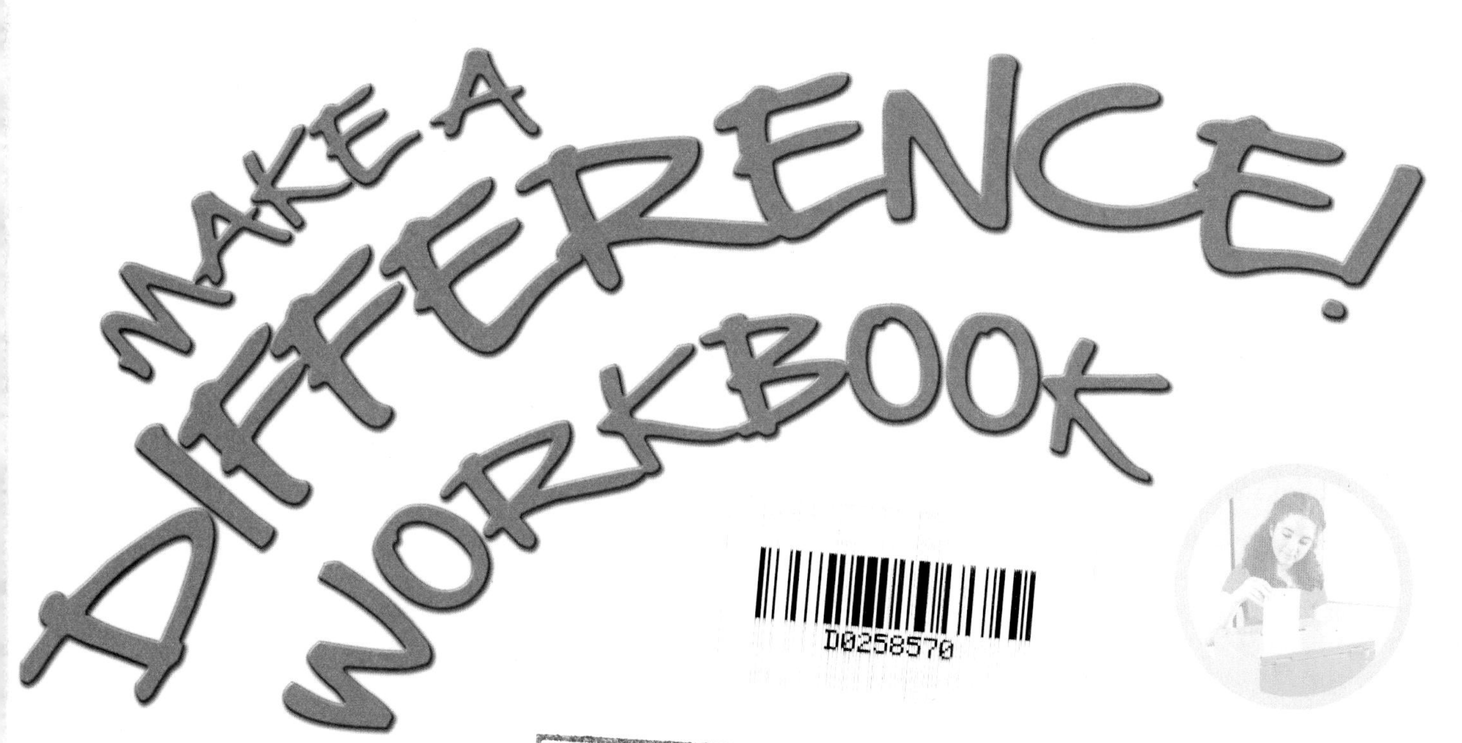

Conor Harrison
and
Máirín Wilson

Editor: Sinéad Keogh

Design and layout: Niamh Carey, Liz White Designs

Illustrations: Emily Skinner (Graham-Cameron Illustration)

ISBN: 978-1-84741-835-7

Folens Publishers
Hibernian Industrial Estate
Greenhills Road
Tallaght
Dublin 24

CONTENTS

Chapter 1: Active Citizenship 1

Chapter 2: Human Dignity 11

Chapter 3: Rights & Responsibilities 21

Chapter 4: Stewardship 43

Chapter 5: Development 60

Chapter 6: Democracy 70

Chapter 7: Law 90

Chapter 8: Interdependence 100

Chapter 9: Guide to Assessment in CSPE 119

Acknowledgements

The authors and Publisher wish to express their thanks to the following for permission to reproduce copyrighted material:

Age Action Ireland;

Alamy;

An Taisce;

Dreamstime;

Fairtrade;

Focus Ireland;

Getty Images;

Irish Guide Dogs;

Irish Traveller Movement;

National Roads Authority;

Pavee Point Traveller Centre;

Ombudsman for Children's Office;

Photocall Ireland;

Reuters;

Simon Community;

St Vincent de Paul;

Thinkstock.

Active Citizenship

Chapter 1

Welcome to CSPE, a new course of study for you over the next three years. It is important that you know what these letters stand for, so fill in the blanks. Welcome to C ____________, S ____________, and P ____________ E ____________.

This is a course about being a citizen. It is based on a belief in human rights and living in a responsible way in the world.

Your CSPE course is built on seven concepts, or ideas: human dignity, rights and responsibilities, stewardship, development, democracy, law and interdependence. You need to know what all these concepts mean. Below is a definition of each one, but they are mixed up. Match the correct definition with the concept.

Concept	Definition
1. Human dignity	A. Is about voting, government and how we are ruled.
2. Rights and responsibilities	B. Is about change for the better and how this change is managed.
3. Stewardship	C. Is about how every person deserves to be respected.
4. Development	D. Is about the way we are linked and connected to people all over the world.
5. Democracy	E. Is about being responsible for the environment.
6. Law	F. Is about human rights and the duties that go with them.
7. Interdependence	G. Is about rules and laws, how they work and what happens if you break them.

Remember that you are already a citizen. This course will help you to understand more about what that means and give you ideas as to how you can be an active citizen, now and in the future.

The Citizenship Rap

Add in your own verse to this rap on the blank lines below, then get together in a group to say the rap aloud.

Citizen, citizen – be a good citizen.

Don't throw litter on the ground
Put it in the bins that are all around.
The world is precious, guard it well
It's under threat, I've heard tell

Citizen, citizen – be a good citizen.

When you are 18 you must go
To cast your vote, to show you know
That you can choose who you want in
To elect the one you want to win.

Citizen, citizen – be a good citizen.

Obey the law, you know it's right
Don't vandalise, rob things or fight
Pay your taxes, careful when you drive,
Know the rules, arrive alive.

Citizen, citizen – be a good citizen.

Care for the old, the homeless, the poor.
Open your heart, be there for sure.
Look out for your neighbours, it's easy to do
Being a good citizen starts with you!

Citizen, citizen – be a good citizen.

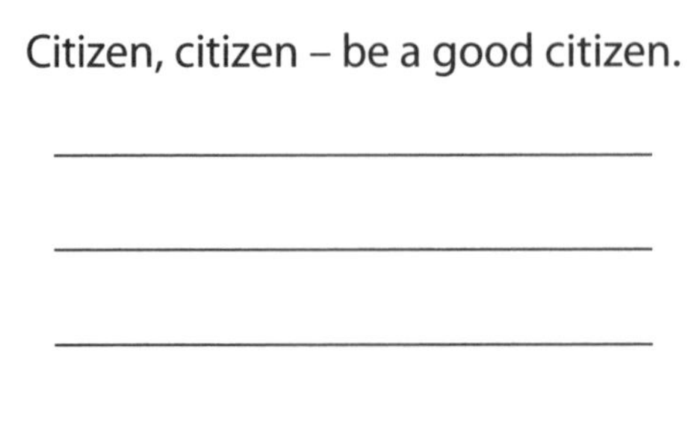

Citizen, citizen – be a good citizen.

Citizens on Parade

The people here are carrying signs about good citizens. Fill in the signs that are blank. Each sign should tell something about being a good citizen.

Understanding Citizenship

Write your answers in the boxes below.

What citizenship is

Why being a good citizen is important

Qualities of a good citizen

What can I do to be a better citizen?

At home

At school

In my community

The Headlines of Today

Newspaper headlines tell about important events.

1. Write down **SIX** real headlines about things happening in the world today. Find two local, two national and two international headlines.
2. Choose **ONE** of the headlines and, in your copy, explain the story behind it.

LOCAL

NATIONAL

INTERNATIONAL

LOCAL

NATIONAL

INTERNATIONAL

What Would a Good Citizen Do?

Write what you could do in each situation below to help the person out.

1. At a supermarket, you see a person pushing a buggy while carrying lots of packages. They are trying to open the door to leave the shop. How could you help?
2. It's your lucky day. You actually got a seat this morning on the bus! As you are going along, an older person gets on. There are no seats left. How could you help?
3. As Pat is walking down the hallway with a stack of books, Fran comes from behind and purposefully bumps into him. Pat stumbles and falls and his books go flying in all directions. Your classmates begin to laugh. How could you help Pat?

Are You a Good Citizen?

Complete the questionnaire below and discuss your answers with ONE other person.

	☺	😐	☹
1. Do you obey the laws of the country?	Yes	Sometimes	Never
2. Do you respect Garda authority?	Yes	Sometimes	Never
3. Do you put graffiti on walls?	Yes	Sometimes	Never
4. Do you always follow the school rules?	Yes	Sometimes	Never
5. Do you throw litter on the ground?	Yes	Sometimes	Never
6. Do you reduce, reuse and recycle?	Yes	Sometimes	Never
7. Do you help your neighbours?	Yes	Sometimes	Never
8. Do you fight with people?	Yes	Sometimes	Never
9. Do you co-operate with your classmates?	Yes	Sometimes	Never
10. Do you take things that don't belong to you?	Yes	Sometimes	Never

Active Citizenship Exam Questions

CSPE Exam Paper 2005, Section 1, Question 2

CSPE Course Concepts

CSPE course concepts:

- Democracy
- Interdependence
- Development
- Stewardship

Each of the meanings given below explains ONE of the course concepts listed above.

Beside each meaning write the name of the concept you think it might explain.

You may write ONE concept only beside each meaning.
You may use each concept only ONCE.

Meaning of Concept	Course Concept
Caring responsibly for our environment and the planet on which we live.	
Government by the people, through voting and elections.	
Improvements taking place in communities at home and abroad.	
The ways in which we are connected with others in the world.	

(4 marks)

CSPE Exam Paper 2009, Section 1, Question 2

CSPE Course Concepts

CSPE is based on seven concepts, as listed below. Beside each concept, write down one ISSUE or TOPIC that relates to that concept. You may use each issue or topic only ONCE.

Rights and Responsibilities: ____________________

Human Dignity: ____________________

Stewardship: ____________________

Development: ____________________

Democracy: ____________________

Law: ____________________

Interdependence: ____________________

(7 marks)

E IT A SWIRL DAY

What is Give it a Swirl Day?

Give It A Swirl Day is the national day of volunteering. It is organised by Volunteer Centres Ireland and other partner organisations.

Give It A Swirl Day is a special project as it is about hands-on involvement rather than fundraising. This gives volunteers an immediate sense of achievement.

For Give It A Swirl Day, we ask organisations to have once-off volunteering opportunities which are good for them and the community. It also shows that volunteering, even for a few short hours, can be a lot of fun and can make a difference.

Volunteers have:

Played bingo, played cards with older people

Cleaned up school grounds,
picked up litter and
raked up the autumn leaves

Invited local people with a disability
to an 'Activity Day'
hosted by their school

Taught older people how to
use their mobile phones or e-mail

Why Get Involved?

- Volunteering is fun and rewarding!
- Great way to develop new skills, team building and leadership!
- You get the chance to make a difference in your community!
- Meet new people who feel strongly about the same issues as you
- Volunteering contributes to a better work-life balance

volunteer centres
Ionaid d'Oibri Deonacha na hÉireann
IRELAND

CSPE Exam Paper 2009, Section 2, Question 1

Study the **Give It A Swirl Day** brochure.

When you have studied this brochure, answer the questions below in your copy.

(a) What is Give It A Swirl Day?

Why is Give It A Swirl Day a special project?

What are organisations encouraged to do for Give It A Swirl Day? *(3 marks)*

(b) From the brochure, name **TWO** volunteering activities that people have done? *(2 marks)*

(c) From the brochure, give **TWO** reasons for getting involved in volunteering? *(2 marks)*

(d) Name and describe a volunteering project (not from the list in the brochure) that **YOUR CSPE CLASS** could undertake as part of this day? *(3 marks)*

(e) In launching the Task Force on Active Citizenship, the then Taoiseach Bertie Ahern said:

'To me an active citizen is one who is aware of what is happening around them and strives towards the common good. It is about accepting a responsibility to help others and being happy to contribute to improve the quality of life of those less fortunate than ourselves.'

Do you agree with this point of view? Explain your answer. *(4 marks)*

CSPE Exam Paper 2007, Section 3, Question 1

Know Your Neighbours Weekend

The Know Your Neighbour campaign has been set up to encourage people to organise an activity and to invite their neighbours to do it. You and some of your friends have decided to organise an event in your neighbourhood to help your neighbours to get to know one another.

(a) Design an invitation that you would send to each of your neighbours, inviting them to your special Know Your Neighbour event. You should include in your invitation at least **THREE** pieces of key information your neighbours would need to know. *(6 marks)*

(b) State and explain **THREE** reasons why you think this campaign is important for people in your neighbourhood. *(6 marks)*

(c) Apart from the invitation, describe in detail **TWO** actions that you and your friends could take in order to promote this Know Your Neighbour event. *(8 marks)*

CSPE Exam Paper 2010, Section 3, Question 3

Active Citizenship Week

Your CSPE class has decided to campaign for an Active Citizenship Week in your community in order to encourage local people to get involved in their own area.

(a) Name **ONE** action that your CSPE class could undertake to promote an Active Citizenship Week in your community.

Describe the work of **TWO** committees/teams that your class might set up in order to promote an Active Citizenship Week in the community. *(6 marks)*

(b) Write a short note of one paragraph to your Principal asking for permission to carry out this action. Explain what you want to do, why you want to do it and what you hope to achieve. *(6 marks)*

(c) You have decided that the theme for your Active Citizenship Week is 'One-for-All and All-for-One'. Design a poster based on this theme to encourage people in your community to get involved in an Active Citizenship Week. *(8 marks)*

A Plain English Guide to Citizenship Terms

1. (a) What is this booklet about?
   (b) What event was being celebrated in 2005? *(2 marks)*
2. (a) What organisation produced this booklet?
   (b) Where does this organisation have its offices? *(2 marks)*
3. Suggest an alternative title for this booklet. *(2 marks)*
4. Describe TWO actions that THE IRISH GOVERNMENT could take to raise awareness about citizens taking a more active role in society. *(4 marks)*

Human Dignity

Chapter 2

Overview of Human Dignity

This concept is about the basic needs that people have because they are born with the dignity of human beings. These needs include such things as clean air and water, proper food and shelter, an education, protection from harm, security, respect and love.

When studying this concept in CSPE, you could look at the many ways people's human dignity is respected and sometimes how it is denied.

On a personal level, we are called to respect the dignity of all human beings and not to discriminate against people because of where they live, how they look, because of their nationality or colour, because of their poverty or wealth, their disabilities or religious beliefs.

Society takes its responsibility very seriously and tries to make sure that nothing happens that reduces human dignity. Governments make sure that laws passed always respect people's dignity.

Sadly, not everybody's human dignity is respected. People are starving and homeless, people are bullied and jeered and people live in poverty. In some parts of the world, people's human dignity is denied to them because of natural disasters like famine or drought, at times of war, where there is a bad leader or because they are living in a country that is still developing.

Needs

1. Match the needs on the left with the words on the right.

air	**shelter**
water	**wear**
a home	**breathe**
clothes	**love**
food	**eat**
friends	**drink**

2. Read the poem below and answer the questions that follow.

I WAS HUNGRY
And you fed your animals with my food.

I WAS HUNGRY
And your multinationals planted your winter tomatoes on our best land.

I WAS HUNGRY
And you wouldn't give up your steak from South America.

I WAS HUNGRY
And they grew coffee for you where corn might grow for my daily meal.

I WAS HUNGRY
But you turned our sugar cane and manioc* into fuel for your cars.

I WAS HUNGRY
But the waste from your factories is poisoning the fishing grounds of the Earth.

I WAS HUNGRY
But with your money you bought up all my food.

I WAS HUNGRY
While my land grows exotic food for your table.

*Manioc is a root vegetable that can be turned into flour.

Source: We Ask Why They Are Hungry, Christian Aid and CAFOD.

3. (a) Name and explain how the needs of any **TWO** groups from this poem were placed before the needs of this hungry person.

   (b) Suggest **ONE** action that **THE IRISH GOVERNMENT** could take to try to end world hunger.

Nine Hours

Source: WaterAid/Mike Wade.

In Burkina Faso, West Africa, Segueda Zouga has no choice but to spend nine hours a day collecting dirty water from a hole. Not only is it unsafe to drink, but the long daily trek means Segueda has no time left to earn a living.

'As soon as the sun rises at 6 a.m., we go to fetch water. We take whatever containers we have down to the dry river bed and dig for water there. It can take three hours to dig deep enough to reach water and we have to go three times a day.

'I have had six children and yet only two of them have survived. My only choice is to give them water which is not safe to drink or no water at all. I worry about the water I give them constantly. All of us get ill often. My children and I get fevers, stomach cramps and diarrhoea. Many people in the village die.

'Water is the overwhelming problem in my life and in the lives of the other families in this village. All day I think about nothing else. At night I go to sleep worrying about fetching water and about what will happen if there is no water for us to fetch tomorrow. All of us go, old women, young women, pregnant women – even the children. We all have to do our bit. I know the children should go to school, but what choice do we have? What use is an education if I can't give my children enough water to drink?'

She looks much older, but Segueda is only 45. She and her two children live with around 35 other people in a mud-walled compound. There are no men among them – they have to spend months away from home looking for labour in the Ivory Coast.

Water is the community's biggest problem, but now WaterAid has plans to work with them and help them build a safe water supply. Once it is complete, life will be different here.

People who have access to clean water and sanitation have better health and more time to improve their children's education, nutrition and family income; they also spend less on medicine. Safe water close to home will mean Segueda no longer has to spend her days on the search for water.

'If I didn't have to spend nine hours a day fetching water, I could do so much more. Sometimes I try to spin the cotton we grow to weave cloth and make clothing, with maybe some left over to sell, but I hardly even have time to do this. If we had water, my children could go to school and I would be able to spend time growing more food and cleaning the compound.'

Sophie and Laurentine live in Bayandi Palogo, where the WaterAid project has already made a huge difference to the lives of people in the community. Laurentine says, 'We have a women's group where we make soap to sell. We also grow peanuts to sell.'

Sophie adds that water, sanitation and hygiene education are giving her hope for the future. 'The building of latrines has brought a lot of changes. And now we have learned a lot about hygiene. Without safe water, the children were often ill, which stopped them going to school. Now I hope that my children will grow up in good health, do well at school and get a job.' Soon we hope Segueda will be able to tell a similar story.

1. Draw **FOUR** pictures/cartoons/images in the boxes provided which illustrate four different aspects of Segueda Zouga's life.

2. What difference would it make to Segueda Zouga's life if she had water easily available to her?

Special Needs Parking

Some parking places have special symbols put on them to remind people that they are only for the use of people with disabilities.

Do you think that this is right?

Explain your answer.

Design your own parking space reminder-card that you could put on the windscreen of a car that parked wrongly in your school car-park in a space meant for a person with disabilities.

Irish Sign Language

Sign language allows deaf people to talk and communicate with each other. From the diagrams below, learn to sign your name.

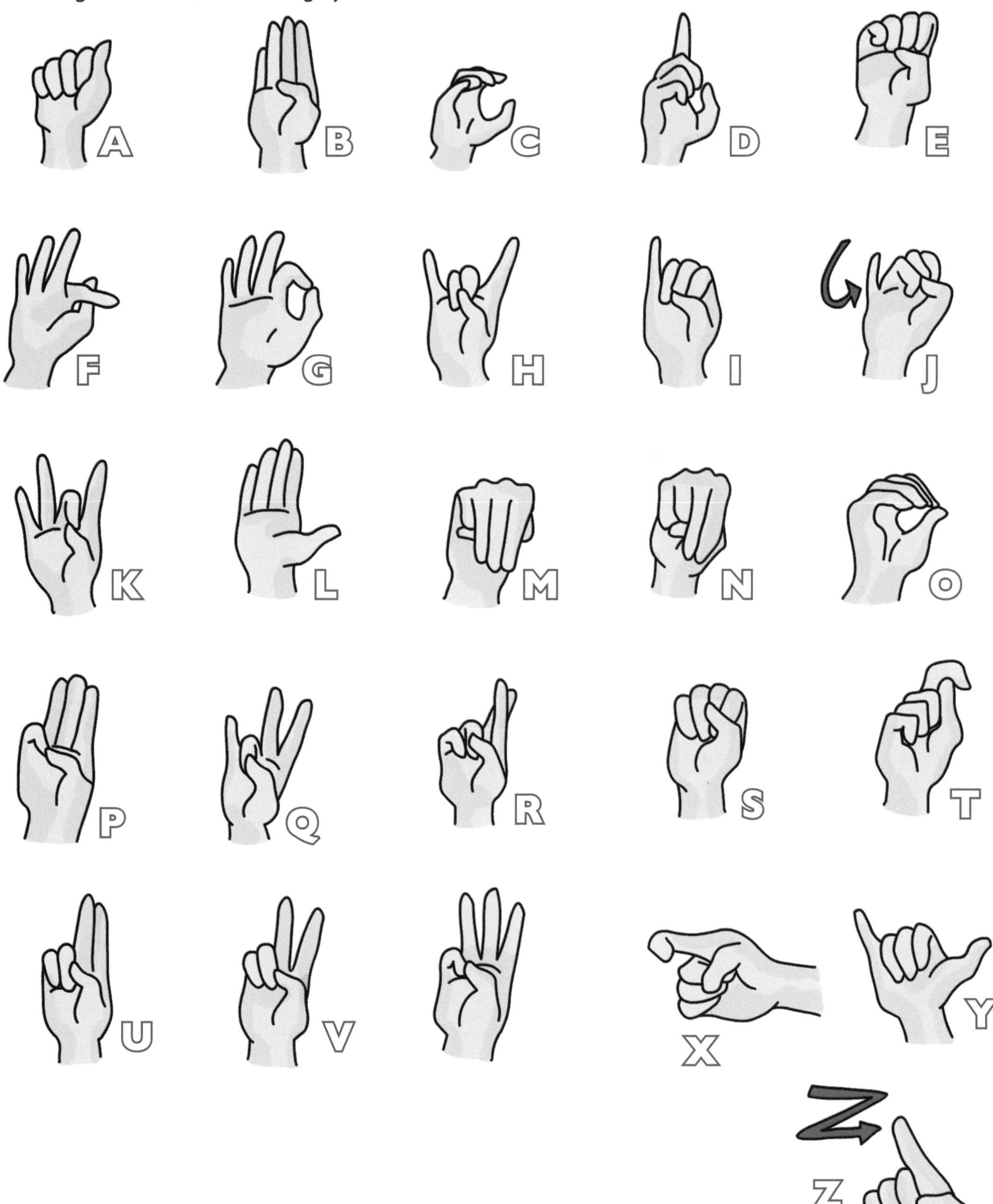

Picture This!

A young child in India walking through mud and dirt to collect water for his family.

Do you really need a picture?

What is the message in this poster? ________________________________

____

____

____

____

Is this poster a good way to get across a message? Explain your answer ______________

____

____

____

____

Human Dignity

Match the person below with the human dignity issue that s/he is devoted to.

You can use each name and issue only once.

Name	Issue
1. John O'Shea	A. Building homes for people living in the townships in South Africa.
2. Bob Geldof	B. Helping those suffering after disasters around the world.
3. Sr Stanislaus Kennedy	C. Working for the homeless.
4. Christina Noble	D. Organising concerts to help fight poverty.
5. Niall Mellon	E. Looking after homeless boys in Dublin.
6. Fr Peter McVerry	F. Looking after street children and building orphanages for them.

Human Dignity Exam Questions

CSPE Exam 2007, Section 1, Question 2

Below are the names of six groups of people and the logos of six organisations with which they are most closely linked. In the space provided beneath each logo, write the name of the group of people with which it is most closely linked.

You may write only ONE name under each logo. You may use the name of each group of people only ONCE.

Groups of People:

- Asylum seekers and refugees
- Homeless people
- Older people
- People who face the death penalty
- Poor people
- The travelling community

(a) Focus Ireland

____

(b) Age Action Ireland

____

(c) Amnesty International

____

(d) Combat Poverty Agency

____

(e) Irish Refugee Council

____

(f) Pavee Point Traveller Centre

____

(6 marks)

Jack and Jill

Study the information on the envelope above, and then answer the questions below in your copy:

1. What organisation is behind this campaign?
2. Name three reasons why it is a good idea to recycle your mobile phone.
3. Describe the three steps you must take to recycle your old mobile phone.
4. How is this campaign linked to the concept of human dignity?

St Vincent de Paul Homelessness Campaign

Every year St Vincent de Paul has a campaign to raise awareness and funds for homeless people in Ireland. Your CSPE class is interested in this and wants to find out more about the campaign. You plan to ask a speaker to visit your school to tell you about this campaign.

(a) Write a letter, or email, to St Vincent de Paul asking for a speaker to come to your school. Give **THREE** reasons why you want the speaker to come, and explain what you hope to get from the visit. *(8 marks)*

(b) You will need teams to organise the visit. Name **THREE** teams your class would put in place and describe the work **EACH** team would have to do. *(6 marks)*

(c) Design a poster with a slogan that you could hang in the room where the speaker would speak to the class, showing that you know how important a campaign on homelessness is in Ireland today. *(6 marks)*

Environmental Disaster

There has been a natural disaster in a faraway country as a result of a volcano which caused a tsunami and then a flood. Millions of people have been left without their basic needs catered for, like clean water, shelter and medicine. Hundreds of thousands of people have died. You and your friends want to do something to help.

(a) Name **ONE** organisation that you could contact that would help out at a time like this. Give **TWO** reasons why you would choose that particular organisation. *(6 marks)*

(b) Write a short article that you would send to your local newspaper trying to get more support for this cause. *(8 marks)*

(c) Describe **TWO** actions that a community could do to help out in a time like this. *(6 marks)*

Chapter 3 Rights & Responsibilities

Overview of Rights and Responsibilities

This concept is easy to understand – the words 'rights' and 'responsibilities' really say it all. It is about the rights that we have as human beings. These rights have been written down in a number of important documents, like the Universal Declaration of Human Rights and the European Convention of Human Rights. It is also about the responsibilities that go hand in hand with our rights.

Rights mean such things as the right to freedom, the right to a name and nationality, the right to opinion, the right to practise your religion and the right to a fair trial.

Children's rights are also named and there is a separate document called the UN Convention on the Rights of the Child which sets out these rights. Many countries have signed up to all these documents. This means that they must take human rights and children's rights into account when they are passing laws.

However, it is a sad fact that in many countries around the world, people's human rights are denied. Not all countries allow freedom to people.

Mutabi Family Under Seige

The Mutabi family came to Ireland from Burkino Faso, in Africa, 10 years ago. Their children were all born in Ireland. Kitzy is aged eight and Sando is aged six. The family moved into a house in Baile Dorcha. Mr Mutabi worked in the local factory before buying a lease on a small shop where he wanted to open a newsagents. One night, about 20 people attacked the Mutabis' home. They smashed windows and shouted racist comments.

Even though the Gardaí keep an eye on the place, the attacks have continued on and off for almost a year. The children are bullied at school and Mrs Mutabi is often afraid to go out. The family lives in constant fear.

1. Look at the following possible actions the Mutabi family can take. For each action, say whether or not the Mutabi family should take this action and what would happen if they did.

Action A They could move out of the area, away from the racist gangs who are attacking their home.

Action A: ______________________________

____

____

____

Action B They could defend their home with a guard dog or shotgun or both.

Action B: ______________________________

____

____

____

Action C They could put steel doors and steel window shutters on their house and turn it into a fortress.

Action C: ______________________________

____

____

____

Action D They could ask the Gardaí to mount a 24-hour guard on their home.

Action D: ______________________________

____

____

____

Action E They could get together with other immigrants in the area and form a vigilante group to fight the racist mob.

Action E: ______________________________

____

____

____

Action F They could go back to live in Burkino Faso.

Action F: ______________________________

____

____

____

Action G They could try to get to know the people who attacked their house. That way, the racists might see that the Mutabis are no different to them, except for the colour of their skin.

Action G: ______________________________

____

____

____

____

2. If you and your family were subjected to racist attacks, what would you do about them?

____

____

____

____

3. Why do people attack homes like the Mutabis'?

____

____

____

____

4. What rights are being denied in this story?

____

____

____

____

Older and Bolder Postcard Campaign

'Time is the only thing that separates each of us from our older self'

Professor Eamon O'Shea, *Director of the Irish Centre for Social Gerontology at the National University of Ireland, Galway*

Your voice counts!! Join the campaign...

Whatever your age, you can make a difference.

We are asking all politicians and political parties to commit to the development of a National Strategy for Older People; a strategy that supports equality, includes the older person's voice, and ends discrimination against older people.

Please sign and stamp the pre-addressed card and return it to us. We will be passing your message on to all the political parties and politicians contesting the next election.

Declaration of support

I call upon all political candidates and political parties to commit to a National Strategy for Older People after the formation of the next government and to include this commitment in their election manifestos.

Older & Bolder Campaign
PO Box 10845
Dublin 9

Support equality for older people

Find out how **www.older&bolder.ie**

When you have studied both sides of the postcard above, answer the following questions.

1. (a) What problem is this postcard campaign raising awareness about?
   (b) What is the campaign website address? *(2 marks)*
2. Name **TWO** of the organisations involved in producing the postcards. *(2 marks)*
3. (a) What strategy are the campaigners asking politicians to develop?
   (b) What is the campaign slogan? *(2 marks)*
4. Besides a postcard campaign, describe actions **OLDER PEOPLE** can take to raise awareness about the rights of older people. *(4 marks)*
5. Older people are one of the groups in Irish society who may be discriminated against. Name **TWO** other groups who are sometimes discriminated against. *(4 marks)*

Refugees

1. How is the person who is third row down, second from the right different from the other people?

____

2. Why are refugees forced to leave their country?

____

3. What do refugees leave behind?

____

4. What does UNHCR stand for?

____

5. What does the UNHCR ask us to do?

____

6. How many refugees are they helping around the world?

____

7. Suggest a suitable campaign slogan to represent the work of the UNHCR.

____

'I Hope They Won't Kill Me'

I HOPE THEY WON'T KILL ME I HOPE NO-BODY'S FOLLOWING ME I HOPE I DON'T STEP ON A LANDMINE I HOPE I FIND SOME WATER SOON I HOPE I DON'T DIE OUT HERE I HOPE SOMEONE WILL FIND ME I HOPE THE UNITED NATIONS CAN HELP ME I HOPE THEY'VE GOT FOOD AND SHELTER I HOPE THEY CAN HELP ME FIND MY FAMILY I HOPE WE'LL BE ABLE TO GO BACK ONE DAY I HOPE WE FIND A PLACE TO CALL HOME I HOPE WE LEARN TO FIT IN I HOPE WE CAN BUILD A FUTURE HERE

I HOPE WE NEVER, EVER, HAVE TO RUN AGAIN!

UNHCR
The UN Refugee Agency

GIVING 19 MILLION REFUGEES REASON TO HOPE

www.unhcr.org

World Refugee Day
20 June

1. What event did the UNCHR put these posters together to raise awareness about?
2. What is the shared theme in both posters?
3. List three things a refugee may hope for.
4. Suggest three reasons why these refugees left home.
5. Describe **TWO** actions that you could take in your community to make refugees more welcome.

Ireland to Evacuate!

Imagine there has been a nuclear catastrophe in Wales. As a result Ireland must be totally abandoned. Vietnam has decided to accept 500 Irish refugees. You are the chairperson of the Vietnamese Resettlement Committee. It is the committee's job to make arrangements for welcoming the refugees from Ireland and for organising support for the next seven years.

You must decide the following.

1. What groups will be on the Resettlement Committee? Give reasons for your answer.

2. What special needs will the refugees from Ireland have? (Consider some of the following: where they will live, language, work, education, welfare benefits, health, culture, contact with each other, religious practice.)

3. What kind of things will have to be done immediately?

Travellers

I was hungry and you blamed it on my parents;
I was thirsty and you went to see the EEC wine lake;
I was sick and you told me to wait;
I was dying and you set up a Commission on Itinerancy,
A Review Body on Travellers, a monitoring Body on what?;
I was naked and you said so were my ancestors;
I had no job and you said we don't employ knackers;
I was all these things and you said it was the will of God;
I was homeless and you sent me a lorry load of stones and a bulldozer;
When did I see you hungry?

Margaret Maughan

1. Make a list of all the ways that the human dignity of Travellers is being denied in this poem.

____

____

____

____

____

2. Imagine you have invited the above poet to visit your school. Write the speech of welcome that you would give.

____

____

____

____

____

____

3. Write out **THREE** questions you would ask the poet about the life of a Traveller.

(a) ______________________________

(b) ______________________________

(c) ______________________________

Pavee Lackeen

When you have studied the DVD cover above, answer the following questions in your copy.

1. (a) What is the subtitle to the *Pavee Lackeen* film?
   (b) According to the information on the DVD cover, what two issues do Winnie and her family have to struggle with day by day? *(3 marks)*
2. (a) What rating was given by the Irish film censors to this film?
   (b) Why do you think real members of the Travelling community acted in this film? *(2 marks)*
3. The film shows the multicultural society on the east coast of Ireland, with Russian video shops, Chinese-run amusement arcades and shops that sell Hindu goods. Yet in this society, the rights of Travellers are still sometimes denied. Suggest **TWO** ways in which the rights of Travellers are still being denied in Ireland today. *(2 marks)*
4. Design a T-shirt that could be sold at the first public showing of *Pavee Lackeen*. *(3 marks)*
5. Outline **TWO** actions that you and **YOUR CSPE CLASS** could take to reduce prejudice and stereotyping towards the Travelling community in Ireland. *(4 marks)*

1. What are these drawings based on?

____

____

____

____

2. What **FOUR** priorities should be given to children, according to this poster?

(a) ______________________________

(b) ______________________________

(c) ______________________________

(d) ______________________________

3. What rights does the poster say all children have?

(a) ______________________________

(b) ______________________________

(c) ______________________________

(d) ______________________________

(e) ______________________________

(f) ______________________________

4. Pick any **FOUR** children's rights and design your own symbols/pictures to go with them.

Ombudsman for Children and Young People

Who is the Ombusdman for Children?

Emily Logan is the first Ombudsman for Children in Ireland.

Emily worked as a children's nurse for 22 years before she became Ombudsman for Children, so she has lots of experience of working with children and young people.

What does the Ombudsman for Children do?

The Ombudsman for Children's Office was set up under the Ombudsman for Children's Act, 2002. The aim of the Ombudsman for Children is to promote and protect the rights and interests of children and young people under the age of 18.

The Ombudsman for Children Act, 2002, describes in detail what the Ombudsman for Children can do. The three main areas of work outlined in the Ombudsman for Children Act, 2002 are:

- Promoting children's rights
- Research and policy
- Complaints and investigations

Ombudsman

for children and young people

Write to us at:
Ombudsman for Children's Office
Millennium House
52-56 Great Strand Street
Dublin 1

or e-mail us at oco@oco.ie
or ring us on Lo-Call 1890 654 654
or (01) 865 6800

From the Office of the Ombudsman for Children

CSPE Exam Paper 2008, Section 2, Question 2

When you have studied the leaflet, answer the following questions in your copy.

(a) Who is the Ombudsman for Children?
Name the Act that set up the Office of Ombudsman for Children.
What is the aim of the Ombudsman for Children? *(3 marks)*

(b) What are the Ombudsman's main areas of work?
What is the email address of the Ombudsman for Children's Office? *(2 marks)*

(c) The UN passed a Convention on the Rights of the Child in 1989 in order to give extra protection to children. Name **THREE** of these rights. *(3 marks)*

(d) Name **TWO** actions that **YOUR SCHOOL** could take in order to hear the opinions of students. *(2 marks)*

(e) Ireland signed the UN Convention in September 1992 and must hear the voices of children and young people.
Describe **TWO** activities that the **IRISH GOVERNMENT** could organise to make sure that the voices and opinions of young people are heard. *(4 marks)*

Mobile Phone Text Bullying

CSPE Exam Paper 2009, Section 3, Question 2

Texting is a great way to stay in touch with your friends and family but sadly it can also be used to bully, harass and frighten people. Text bullying can be texts that frighten, insult, threaten you or make you feel uncomfortable. Your CSPE class has decided to do some work on this issue.

(a) Write a short article for your school newsletter in which you give **THREE** pieces of advice about what students should do if they receive a bullying text message. *(6 marks)*

(b) Name an Action Project that **YOUR CSPE CLASS** could undertake on this issue and describe **THREE** tasks your class would do as part of this action. *(8 marks)*

(c) Name and describe **THREE** other actions that **YOUR SCHOOL** could take to help prevent text bullying in your school. *(6 marks)*

Bullying

1. What is bullying? Fill in the speech bubbles.

2. Choose **ONE** of the actions listed here and describe how your CSPE class could get involved in it.

1. Have an anti-bullying week.
2. Go online and get information on bullying and make a display.
3. Run an anti-bullying poster campaign.
4. Have an anti-bullying assembly.
5. Invite in a guest speaker on bullying.
6. Lobby your student council to get a policy on bullying.
7. Set up a support service for victims of bullying.
8. Write a song or poem to highlight bullying.

What would you like your school to do?

Action chosen: ______________________________

Description: ______________________________

____

____

____

STOP Child Labour

www.schoolisthebestplacetowork.org

Facts and Figures

Child Labour involves children in the making of bricks, working with machinery in agriculture and carpet weaving, in domestic labour, in the sex industry, in construction work, in deep-sea fishing and in the making of matches and fireworks and hundreds of other activities that deny children the right to full-time education.

1 in every 6 people aged between 5 and 17 years is defined as a child labourer

CSPE Exam Paper 2005, Section 2, Question 3

When you have studied the poster on the previous page, answer the following questions in your copy.

(a) Child Labour denies children the right to what?

How many young people between the ages of 5 and 17 are defined as child labours?

What is the website address for this campaign to stop child labour? *(3 marks)*

(b) Name **THREE** different types of work in which child labourers are involved. *(3 marks)*

(c) The Protection of Young Persons (Employment) Act, 1996 states that the maximum weekly working hours are 0 hours for 14 year olds and 8 hours for 15 year olds during school term-time and 35 hours per week during holidays.

Give one reason why you think this law was brought in. *(2 marks)*

(d) The International Labour Organisation estimates that 246 million children between the ages of 5 and 17 years of age are working as child labourers. Most of these children are in Asia (60%) and in Africa (32%).

Suggest **ONE** action **THE IRISH GOVERNMENT** could take to help reduce the number of child labourers. *(2 marks)*

(e) As a citizen of Ireland you can also play a role. Suggest **TWO** actions **YOU** could take to inform people in your community about child labour. *(4 marks)*

CSPE Exam Paper 2000, Section 3, Question 4

A well known speaker from a human rights organisation has been invited to speak at your school. You have been asked to give a short speech introducing this person.

(a) Write this speech. In it, you should mention a number of different points. Some of these points should refer to the organisation that this person represents and the type of work that it does.

(b) How would you judge whether the visit was a success or not?

(c) Describe a CSPE Action Project that you could do with your chosen organisation.

Who Is Responsible?

Look at each of the broken items numbered 1 to 8 and answer the following questions for each item:

(a) Why was this item useful?

(b) Who might be affected because it is broken?

(c) Who has the responsibility to do something about it?

1.

2.

3.

4.

5.

6.

7.

8.

Responsible Pet Owners

Toby the terrier said, 'I know what I want for Christmas. I want a child.'

'You're not getting a child and that's that!' barked Mrs Terrier. 'How many times do I have to tell you? It costs too much money to keep a child. We can't afford one.'

'Ah, Mam, let him get a child,' said Mimi, Toby's sister. 'A cute little child, with bright eyes and curly hair.'

'No, no,' said Mrs Terrier. 'A child has to be looked after and fed. It needs exercise and attention. I know who would end up doing it all – me, as usual! You have no idea what a can of people food costs these days. You can't just feed them on scraps, you know. Who'll mind the child when we go away, I ask you?'

'The Sheepdog family down the road have two fully grown people,' whined Toby.

'The Sheepdogs are better off than we are. You can't have a child just because they have one.'

Mimi began to whimper a little and Mrs Terrier said, 'Well, okay, I'll talk to your father when he gets in, but don't go building your hopes up. Now go and watch *Lassie* on TV.'

1. What responsibilities did Mrs Terrier point out to Toby and Mimi about having a child pet?

____

____

2. How is the story like a child wanting to get a puppy?

____

____

3. Give this story a different title.

____

4. What do you think?

____

____

Human Rights Activists

Place photographs of the **EIGHT** Human Rights Activists from Ireland and abroad in the boxes provided below.

1. Bono	2. Adi Roche
3. Aung San Suukyi	4. Nelson Mandela
5. Paul Rusesabagina	6. Mary Robinson
7. Christina Noble	8. Colm O'Gorman

Interview with a Human Rights Activist

Choose any human rights activist from Chapter 3 of *Make A Difference!* and imagine that he or she is coming on a visit to your school. You are going to interview this person.

1. Write out **FOUR** questions that you would ask your visitor, and from the detail in Chapter 3, write out the answers that he or she might give.

Questions	**Answers**
A ______	A ______
B ______	B ______
C ______	C ______
D ______	D ______

2. Over the next few years, you might invite many speakers to talk to you about CSPE issues, so design the cover of a Visitors' Book for your classroom.

Human Rights Organisations

Below are the names of **EIGHT** groups of people and the logos of **EIGHT** organisations with which they are most closely linked. In the space provided under each logo, write the name of the group of people with which it is most likely linked.

- Homeless people
- Children who want to have their rights met
- Members of the Travelling Community
- People facing the death penalty
- Older people
- People seeking asylum and refugees
- Blind people
- Women

(a)

ombudsman
for children • do leanaí

____

(b)

____

(c)

____

(d)

____

(e)

____

(f)

____

(g)

____

(h)

____

National Holocaust Memorial Day / European Day Against Genocide

When you have studied the poster above, answer the questions below in your copy.

1. (a) 27th January is a special designated day. What event is remembered on this day in Ireland?
   (b) What is the poster campaign encouraging us to do? *(2 marks)*
2. The poster shows different groups of people who have been victims of genocide. Name **TWO** groups who have been victims of genocide. *(2 marks)*
3. (a) Why is it said that the cry of 'Never Again!' has a hollow ring to it?
   (b) What does the term 'racism' mean? *(2 marks)*
4. **YOUR CSPE CLASS** has decided to mark European Day against Genocide. Suggest **TWO** actions you could take in your school to raise awareness about genocide. *(4 marks)*
5. 'Racism and prejudice exist everywhere, including the town in which you live.' Describe **TWO** actions **YOUR COMMUNITY** could take to bring people together to celebrate their differences. *(4 marks)*

Protecting Human Rights

On 28th August 1963, Martin Luther King, Jr made his now famous 'I have a dream' speech in which he spoke about human rights and equal opportunities for all people, no matter what their skin colour.

Your CSPE class would like to raise awareness about Martin Luther King's 'I have a dream' speech through organising an exhibition.

(a) Give **THREE** reasons why you think an exhibition would be a good way of raising awareness about Martin Luther King, Jr. *(6 marks)*

(b) Design a cover for a guide booklet to the exhibition that you would give to each person visiting the exhibition. You should include a suitable title for the booklet, with a drawing or picture in your design. *(6 marks)*

(c) Describe **TWO** other actions that **YOUR CSPE CLASS** could undertake to make people aware of Martin Luther King, Jr and his work for human rights. *(8 marks)*

Amnesty International

AMNESTY
INTERNATIONAL

Amnesty International is Ireland's largest human rights organisation with 15,000 members in Ireland and 2.8 million members worldwide. Amnesty works in 150 countries around the globe.

(a) Write a short speech for a school assembly explaining why the work of Amnesty International is so important. Give **THREE** reasons why your class thinks it is important. *(6 marks)*

(b) You have decided to make a poster to raise awareness about the work of Amnesty International. Design a poster which will explain in words and pictures what Amnesty International is about. *(6 marks)*

(c) Besides poster-making, name and describe **TWO OTHER** actions that **YOUR CSPE CLASS** could take in your school to highlight the work of Amnesty International. *(8 marks)*

Stewardship

Chapter 4

Overview of Stewardship

Learning about being a good citizen is also about learning to care for the environment. Stewardship is a word that is used to describe responsibility for the environment. It means that we are given responsibility for the world for the years we live on the Earth and that it is up to us to pass this Earth on, in a healthy state, to the next generations. Over time, the planet has suffered and many problems are facing the world today. Issues like climate change, greenhouse gases, holes in the ozone layer and global warming are repeatedly in the news.

The problems facing the Earth are big issues for governments and many laws are passed to try to protect the world. For example, governments have environmental policies on waste and carbon emissions. National groups like ENFO, An Taisce and Friends of the Earth are devoted to the care and protection of the Irish environment.

In local communities, people work together to care for the environment – Green Schools are set up, Tidy Towns committees work hard to keep areas tidy and other local groups like residents' associations work to make areas look clean and cared for.

But stewardship comes right down to the individual – you can play your part in caring for the environment. How? It might surprise you to learn that the things you do, like dropping litter or using certain sprays, can affect the whole world. You can also care for the environment by using your power as a consumer (buyer of goods), such as choosing things with less packaging or packaging that can by recycled and by being responsible in the ways you get rid of things once they are used up or you have no more need for them. This is when you can choose to reuse, to reduce, to repair and to recycle. Years ago, things were made to last for a long time, but now we live in a world where things are disposable and have a short lifespan. So we are creating more and more waste.

Animals are part of the environment and we have a duty to care for and protect them. We also have to respect their rights and make sure that we don't cause them harm or suffering or cause them to become extinct by our actions. Being a steward of the planet is one responsibility of being a good citizen.

Environmental Poems

Great Green Limericks

There was a young green from Glenties
Who worried about CFCs.
He said, 'I object
To the Greenhouse Effect
Which is heating us up by degrees.'

Complete the following Limerick:

One day when the petrol runs out

____

____

____

____

There was a young man from Brazil
Who cut down the trees on a hill.
It rained all one day
And the soil washed away
So life on the hill now is nil.

Now write your own Limerick from start to finish:

____

____

____

____

____

The Newcomer

'There's something new in the river,'
The fish said as it swam.
'It's got no scales, no fins, no gills.
And ignores the impassable dam.'

'There's something new in the trees.'
I heard a bloated thrush sing,
'It's got no beak, no claws, no feathers,
And not even the ghost of a wing.'

'There's something new in the warren,'
The rabbit said to the doe,
'It's got no fur, no eyes, no paws.
Yet digs deeper than we can go.'

'There's something new in the whiteness.'
Said the snow-bright polar bear,
'I saw its shadow on a glacier
But it left no footprints there.'

Throughout the animal kingdom
The news was spreading fast –

No beak, no claws, no feathers,
No scales, no fur, no gills,
It lives in the trees and the water.
In the earth and the snow and the hills,
And it kills and it kills and it kills.

Gargling with Jelly,
Brian Patten

1. Name the different creatures mentioned in the poem.

____

____

2. What is 'The Newcomer'?

____

____

Earth Damage Report

Divide up into six small groups. Each group should read through **ONE** Earth Damage Report on pages 92–94 of *Make A Difference!* and then prepare a radio or television news item/programme on this topic using the Earth Damage Report information. Then you should perform your piece for the class.

Programme introduction:

____

____

____

____

____

Piece of Music/Poem: Title: ______________ Time: ______________

Why this piece was chosen: ______________________________

____

____

____

Person you have chosen to interview: Name: ______________________

Why you have chosen this person: ______________________________

____

____

____

What this person has to say about your Earth Damage Report: ______________

____

____

____

____

____

____

Climate Change

When you have studied the brochure above, answer the following questions in your copy.

1. According to the brochure:
   (a) Why is the bus the best way to travel?
   (b) How much does a lagging jacket cost?
   (c) How many traditional lightbulbs does a CFL light bulb replace? *(3 marks)*
2. (a) How much does the brochure say can be saved in a well-insulated house?
   (b) Why is wind-generated electricity good for the environment? *(3 marks)*
3. Why is a penguin using sunglasses being used in this campaign? *(2 marks)*
4. Governments all around the world are concerned about climate change. Why is climate change such a cause for worry? *(2 marks)*
5. Apart from this brochure campaign, outline **TWO** other ways that the **ORGANISERS OF THIS CAMPAIGN** could raise awareness about the issue of climate change. *(4 marks)*

The Three Rs

Explain the **THREE Rs** and give examples below.

JumbleTown

FREE FURNITURE!

(and lots of other items for the home, workplace and school) available for collection in your locality from

www.jumbletown.ie

Some of the items are new; most are good-quality second-hand

You can also give away items on this eco-website. Its main aim is to promote the practice of life-cycling before costly recycling or disposal.

JumbleTown is good for you, the community and the environment.

1. What is the main aim of JumbleTown?

___

2. What can you get at JumbleTown?

___

3. How do you contact JumbleTown?

___

4. What is the slogan for JumbleTown?

___

5. Who benefits from JumbleTown?

___

6. How is JumbleTown good for the environment?

___

7. In your copy design a new poster to advertise JumbleTown.

Organising a Make Do and Mend Campaign

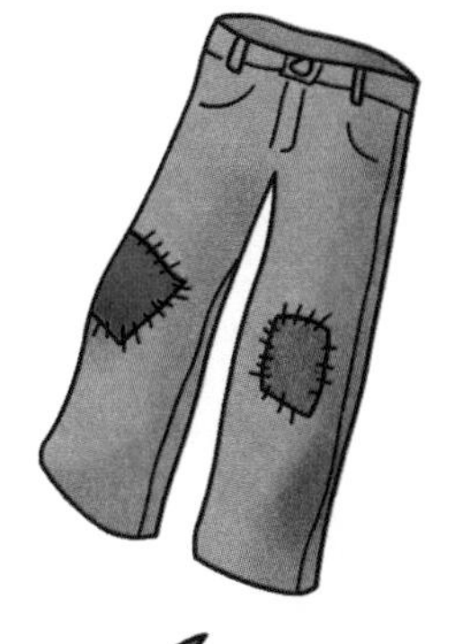

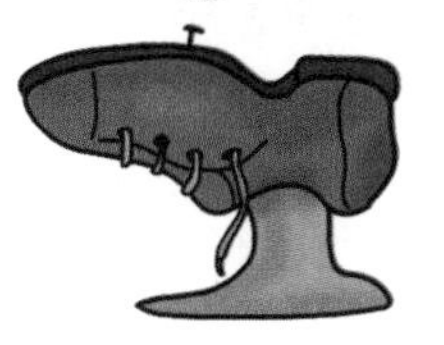
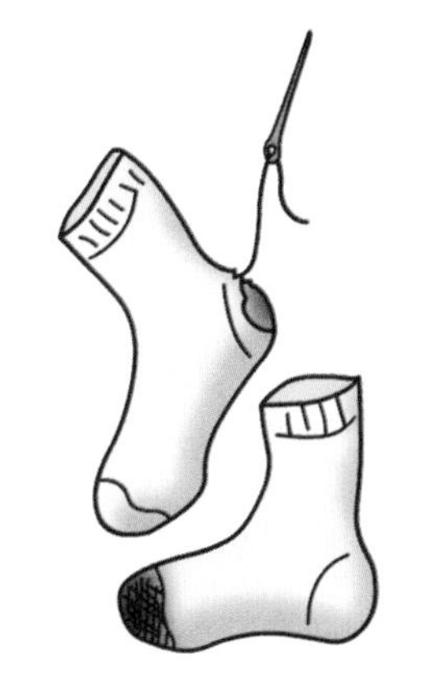

In the past during times of war, many things were hard to get and were in short supply, things like soap, clothes, fuel, butter and fruit. People were given tips for making things last a bit longer – clothes were cut down to fit other children, people mended their shoes, darned their socks and so on. 'Make Do and Mend' was the answer. It encouraged people to become more aware and not to waste anything.

Plan a new campaign for your community that will encourage people to be less wasteful. How will you get your message out to the people? Make up a catchy slogan for your campaign.

My Plan

____

____

____

____

____

____

My Slogan

____

____

A Litter-free Zone

(a) Farmer Frank

(b) Peter Parent

(c) Roger Right

(d) Danielle Don't Care

(e) Sonia Sloppy

(a) Farmer Frank

(b) Peter Parent

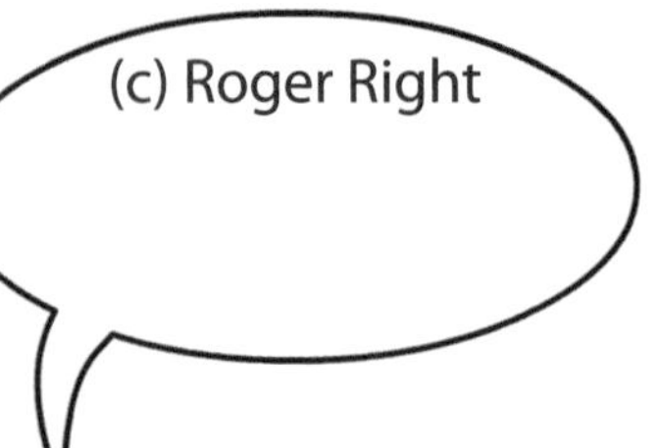

(d) Danielle Don't Care

You are the local Litter Warden. Write a reply to each of the characters above.

Anti-Litter Day

1. You want to organise an Anti-Litter Day in your school. Describe the steps you would take to organise such a day.

2. Design a poster, in the space below, advertising your Anti-Litter Day.

3. Think of a new idea for reducing rubbish.

4. Give your reasons for thinking this is a good idea.

5. What problems would you have to solve to make this idea work?

Nobody Likes Litterbugs

When you have studied the poster above, answer the following questions in your copy.

1. (a) What is this poster's message?
   (b) What organisation produced this poster? *(2 marks)*
2. This poster has a very important message in it. Do you think it is a good poster for getting its message across? Explain your answer. *(2 marks)*
3. Name **THREE** ways of contacting the organisation that produced this poster. *(3 marks)*
4. If your class wanted to do something to tackle the litter problem in your area, suggest **THREE** actions you could take. *(3 marks)*
5. Draw a poster for an Anti-Litter Day campaign in your own school. Along with a drawing/picture, you should include a slogan that will encourage students not to litter. *(4 marks)*

Stop the Assault on our Environment

CSPE Exam Paper 2006, Section 2, Question 1

When you have studied the brochure above, answer the following questions in your copy.

(a) What is the name of the organisation concerned with the environment?
What slogan is used to get the organisation's message across?
Name **THREE** ways of contacting the organisation. *(3 marks)*

1. From this brochure, state **THREE** concerns which this organisation has about the environment. *(3 marks)*
2. 'Treat the earth well: It was not given to you by your parents, it was given to you on loan by your children.' Native American saying.

   What does this saying tell us about the meaning of stewardship? *(2 marks)*
3. By making small changes in the way we live, we can make a big difference to the environment.

   Suggest **TWO** practical steps **YOU** can take to help protect the environment. *(2 marks)*
4. The Tidy Towns Competition each year encourages communities to look after their local environment.

   Describe **TWO** actions **A TIDY TOWNS COMMITTEE** could take to encourage people in a community to look after the local area. *(4 marks)*

Do Animals Have Rights?

A chicken shed in a battery factory can hold up to 30,000 birds. They live there for about 50 days before they are killed for meat. There are often no windows in the shed. The light comes from dull bulbs. Big fans suck out the stale air in the summertime. Most of the birds sit quietly, stretching out a leg from time to time. The farmer watches the light all the time. If it gets too dark, the birds won't eat; if it gets too bright, the birds peck at each other. In fact, the farmer often doesn't even go into the shed. Heat, light and food are all controlled from outside the chicken shed.

1. Do animals have rights? Explain your answer.

   ____

   ____

   ____

2. In what way is battery farming cruel to animals?

   ____

   ____

   ____

3. As consumers of chickens and eggs, how do we benefit from battery farming?

   ____

   ____

   ____

4. Free range is the opposite of battery farming. What does 'free range' mean?

   ____

   ____

   ____

Animal Rights: Who Is Watching Who?

This is a gorilla who has lived for many years in a zoo. All in all, there are about 475 gorillas in captivity. Some zoos keep gorillas who live in very poor, cramped conditions, but others have learned to provide very well for these animals. Some gorillas live for 40 years in zoos.

1. If this gorilla could speak, what would he say about people? Remember, all he would know about people would be what he had learned from being watched in the zoo.

____

____

2. What kind of animal could suffer most from being kept in a zoo?

____

____

3. If pets could talk, what would they say about people?

____

____

In Barcelona Zoo, Spain in 1984, a man was put into a cage to see how visitors would react to him. The man was told to do nothing special. He just behaved normally. He ate, washed, slept and so on. The funny thing was that people spent ages looking at him and seemed just as curious about the human as they were about the other animals in the zoo.

4. Why do you think people did this?

____

____

____

5. What purpose do zoos serve?

____

____

____

It's a Dog's Life!

Take a look at the poster below of 'It's a Dog's Life!' where we see what life is like for two different dogs and their owners. This poster comes from www.dogtrust.ie.

Now imagine you are a pet owner. Choose **ONE** of the following animals and create your own cartoon strip showing the rights of the animal and your responsibilities as a pet owner.

Horse	Parrot	Mouse
Cat	Hamster	Guinea Pig
Budgie	Rabbit	Pigeons

Plan how many boxes you will need before you start.

Don't Go to the Circus Campaign

The ISPCA believes that circuses cannot always provide enough space and proper conditions to guarantee the wellbeing of their animals. They believe that circuses are cruel and unnecessary. You and members of your community have decided to protest to your local authority about the use of land in your area for the staging of a circus using animals.

(a) Draw a sketch of a poster that you would use to notify your community of a public meeting to be held to organise the protest. You should include a slogan referring to the Don't Go to the Circus Campaign in your sketch, with a drawing or picture. *(6 marks)*

(b) Write a letter to your local authority objecting to the staging of the circus in your area. In your letter, suggest **THREE** animal welfare reasons why this circus should not be allowed to perform. *(6 marks)*

(c) Describe the work of **THREE** committees/groups that you would set up in order to organise your protest. *(8 marks)*

CSPE Exam Paper 2005, Section 3, Question 1

Celebrate Earth Day

Senator Nelson, an American politician, thought up the idea of having a special day to do something about what is happening to the environment. The first Earth Day happened in the USA on 22nd April 1970 and is now celebrated around the world on that date.

As part of your learning about stewardship of the environment, your CSPE class has decided to celebrate Earth Day.

(a) Draw a sketch of a poster that you would use to raise awareness about Earth Day. You should include a suitable slogan in your sketch, with a drawing or picture. *(6 marks)*

(b) Write a short article for your school magazine explaining why Earth Day is important. In your article mention at least **TWO** different reasons for getting involved. *(6 marks)*

(c) Describe **TWO** practical actions your CSPE class could take on Earth Day to encourage people in your community to look after their environment. *(8 marks)*

Magic Lamp

Imagine you can have **THREE** wishes for the environment.

Write your wishes in the clouds below.

Chapter 5 Development

Overview of Development

Development and change are all around us. Ask anybody in Ireland and they will tell you just how much Ireland has developed recently, such as new roads, buildings, businesses, factories, houses, apartments, new types of transport, more computers, mobile phones and technology to name just a few examples.

Around the world, countries are changing and developing. In some places the change is rapid, while in others it is much slower. Some places are called 'developing countries' because their development is at a slower pace compared to more developed states. Some of these countries have problems that are linked to famine, poverty, natural disaster and corrupt leaders.

Much development is planned. Governments, local authorities and communities spend a lot of time planning for successful development. However, sometimes people have very different points of view when it comes to planning.

Development usually means change for the better, but when you study this concept you will learn that this is not always the case.

Time Capsule

Imagine you are going to bury a time capsule in your school (or back garden). Its contents should show people in 2100 what life was like in Ireland this year.

1. What ten items would you select to bury? Why?
2. When you have made your list, compare it with one other person in your class. Then agree ten items between you.

3. Write a note that you would put into the time capsule for the person opening it in 2100.

____

____

____

____

____

____

The Good Old Days: My World in the Year 2060

In 2060 I'll be a farmer. I'll have a dip and fences for my cattle. I'll have crop rotation and fertilizers. I hope to do a lot for the country so everyone will have a lot of food.

Tom Odhiambo (16), Kenya

Tracy Cernan (15), USA

I don't ever want to be broke. I'll need to get a good job to earn enough money to keep the lifestyle I've grown up with. I guess by 2060 the United States will be even more powerful.

My feather alarm tickles my feet. I get up and my robot, Gaston, serves breakfast. Electronic life is okay, but boring. I take my helicopter to work and check that the orders I gave yesterday are obeyed.

Valerie Bouget (15), France

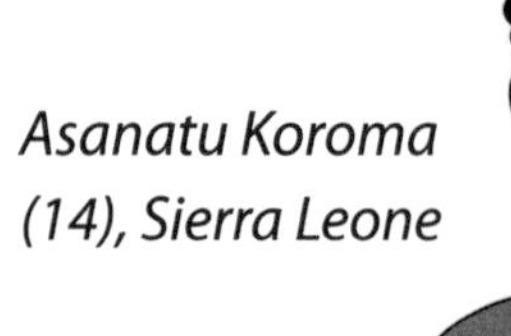

Asanatu Koroma (14), Sierra Leone

The houses will be made of stone. They will cost €500 and will last a long time. The roads will be made of tar. There won't be any beggars or poor people. Everyone will have jobs and food.

1. How do the future views of the four young people differ?

____

____

____

____

2. Imagine that you are 90 years old, looking back on your lifetime. What developments do you think will have taken place so that you will think of now as the 'good old days'?

____

____

____

____

The Lorry Park Protest Meeting

When the people in Ballybeag heard about the plan for the articulated lorry park, they were very angry. Pádraig Brennan organised a protest meeting in Scoil Bríde school hall. They were worried that the plan for the lorry park would go ahead. Here are some of the things that were said at that meeting.

I think we should all write to An Taoiseach and say we won't be pushed around.

Paul Wallace

If they come to build this lorry park, I'm going to chain myself to the bulldozer.

Damien Foster

We should ring up RTÉ and TV3 and the local radio stations. We need lots of publicity if we are to stop this development.

Dave Byrne

We should get everybody in town to sign a petition and send it to the county council.

Alison Ní Shé

We should all go out late at night and paint slogans on the wall, like 'Hands Off Our Street'.

Joan Williams

We need to do something dramatic. If we blocked off Main Street with cars, it would cause a massive traffic jam. Then they'd take notice.

Michelle Nolan

1. In the following table, fill in whether each action is lawful, unlawful or dangerous.

Protest	Lawful	Unlawful	Dangerous
Alison Ní Shé			
Paul Wallace			
Damien Foster			
Dave Byrne			
Michelle Nolan			
Joan Williams			

2. Which of the **SIX** actions do you think would be most effective? Why?

____

____

3. If you had been at the protest meeting, what action would you have suggested?

____

____

Dear Councillor

Finish off the letter below by writing down your ideas to help make your local community a better place.

Dear Councillor,

In our CSPE class we have been talking about our local community, about all the different people in it, about the shops, businesses and services available. We think our community could be made better by

____

____

____

____

____

____

____

____

____

____

____

____

The name of our class is ______________________ and our school is called ______________________. We would be delighted to welcome somebody from the council to the school if you would like to discuss our ideas with us.

Yours faithfully,

____

Planning

Community Centre for Ballyouth

Ballyouth Council agreed last week that they were going to build a new community centre. Councillor Sorcha O'Reilly said last week, 'It's about time some money was spent on the youth of our town. Young people today don't have enough to do. That's why they turn to vandalism, drugs and crime.'

The community centre will have a swimming pool and sports hall for badminton, table tennis and weight training.

At the moment, the nearest swimming pool is in Ballyolder, 10 km away. Ballyouth Community School opens their sports hall to the public, but only during the evenings and at weekends.

Councillor O'Reilly said she would be interested to hear the views of any young people in the area.

Ciara O'Brien

I have a moped. I think the money should be spent on a workshop so we can learn to mend our bikes.

Jessica Kelly

I think the council should build a snooker hall. Snooker is very popular with young people here.

Rebecca Harrington

At the moment, there's nothing for young people to do in Ballyouth, so we wander around the shopping centre. I think we need somewhere to go where we can chat and have a cup of coffee.

Jimmy Kennedy

Most of my friends spend their time playing in the arcades. What we need is somewhere else to go.

Kevin Sweeney

I think there's too much money spent on sport. I hate sport. I think young people in Ballyouth need somewhere to have a disco.

Seamus Forde

I think Ballyouth needs a skating rink.

Write a note to Councillor O'Reilly to tell her what you think of her plan. Use the ideas above and add any ideas of your own.

Dear Ms O'Reilly,

____

____

____

____

____

____

____

____

CSPE Exam 2009, Section 2, Question 4

The Niall Mellon Township Trust

When Niall Mellon saw first-hand the poverty in the townships in South Africa, he set up the Niall Mellon Township Trust in 2002 to provide homes to the poor communities in the townships. Volunteers from Ireland raise money and travel to South Africa to build houses in the townships.

From this...

...to this!

- Living in a shack has been shown to have a negative impact on health, education and self-esteem.
- Without a sense of home, peoples' self-respect can be diminished
- Without basic housing, families are not equipped to face the other challenges poverty brings like crime, poor education, inadequate nutrition, decaying neighbourhoods and sub-standard healthcare.

in partnership with

Most of the workforce comes from the townships themselves. Community development is a central part of the work of the Niall Mellon Township Trust working with local communities in the planning and design of the new communities.

Adapted from: www.irishtownship.com

Study the Niall Mellon Township Trust information leaflet above.

When you have studied this information leaflet, answer the questions below in your copy.

(a) What inspired Niall Mellon to set up this Trust?
In what year was the Niall Mellon Township Trust set up?
What does the Niall Mellon Township Trust do? *(3 marks)*

(b) From your reading of the information leaflet name **THREE** challenges that poverty brings. *(3 marks)*

(c) Why do you think it is important for local communities to get involved in projects like the Niall Mellon Township Trust? *(2 marks)*

(d) A teacher from your school has volunteered to travel to South Africa to build houses with the Niall Mellon Township Trust. Name and describe **ONE** fundraising activity **YOUR SCHOOL** could undertake to help this teacher. *(2 marks)*

(e) Name and describe **TWO** other actions **YOUR COMMUNITY** could take that would help make it possible for this teacher to go to South Africa. *(4 marks)*

Beekeeping Development Programme

Eritrea's six-year-old beekeeping development programme has reached an important target with the delivery of the 1000th colony from the Queen Bee centre in Mendefera in Africa. This is one of three centres in Africa that is trying to help people to make a living in farming communities. Although the environment and the climate continue to make bee-keeping very difficult and sometimes as many as 20% of the hives disappear, yet the project has been a success. By giving training, support and a lot of help with planting crops such as sunflowers, rapeseed and euphoria, hundreds of farming families have been helped to set up beekeeping businesses. Work is under way to organise hive owners into honey producers in Maekel, Emni Haili and in the south of Eritrea.

Adapted from *Self Help Africa Newsletter*

(a) What important target has been reached in Mandefera?

(b) Where is Mendefera?

(c) What **TWO** problems are making bee-keeping very difficult?

(d) Name two ways that families are being helped to set up successful beekeeping businesses.

(e) Why, in your opinion, do organisations help people to set up businesses like this?

(f) In a time of recession some people think that aid should not be given to other developing countries. What do you think? Explain your answer.

Development

1. Match the organisation below with the development work that it is devoted to. You can use each organisation and development work **only once**.

a. Bóthar	1. An American organisation that provides aid for development abroad.
b. Self Help Africa	2. Sends animals to Africa to help people set up in farming.
c. USAID	3. Organises sporting events to support development in Africa.
d. An Taisce	4. Helps people in Africa to improve their own lives and to make a better living.
e. GOAL	5. Watching over the Irish environment and especially new developments being planned.

2. Put the correct words into the sentences below:

Sustainable Development Irish Aid The Local Authority
European Development Agency Agenda 21

(a) _______ _____________ _______________ grants or denies permission for new building, extensions and change of use for land.

(b) _______________ _______________ means that development is planned so as to make sure that the future of the planet, and the people on it, are safe.

(c) To plan for this century the Irish government produced _______________ _________.

(d) ___________ ___________ is part of the Department of Foreign Affairs.

_______________ _______________ _______________ plans for development in EU countries.

3. Explain the difference between the developed world and the developing world.

____

____

____

____

____

____

____

____

____

____

CSPE Exam 2005, Section 3, Question 1

Section 3 Questions

Save the Round Tower Campaign

There is a round tower in your area that has survived the attacks of the Vikings, but now this tower is under threat if a planning application for a development of shops and businesses gets the go-ahead from the local authority. You and members of your community agree that this tower is of great benefit to the community.

(a) Write **THREE** arguments that you would put in a campaign leaflet to stop the planned development in your area. *(6 marks)*

(b) Write a letter to your local authority objecting to the proposed development. In your letter, suggest **TWO** other development proposals for this important site. Explain how these developments will be good for the community. *(6 marks)*

(c) Describe **TWO** actions that **YOUR COMMUNITY** could undertake as part of its campaign to save the round tower. *(8 marks)*

CSPE Exam 2008, Section 3, Question 3

Motorway Development

The National Roads Authority (NRA) has announced that a new motorway is to be built. The route chosen crosses an area where important wildlife will be threatened. You and members of your community have decided to campaign for a different route for the new motorway.

(a) Write a letter to your local Councillor objecting to the planned route through this important environmental area. In your letter make **THREE** arguments against the route that has been chosen. *(6 marks)*

(b) Apart from letter writing, describe **THREE** actions your community could take as part of the campaign to get a different route for the motorway. *(6 marks)*

(c) Name and explain **TWO** skills that you would use while campaigning against the proposed motorway development. *(8 marks)*

Closing a Rural Post Office

Plans have been announced to close your local post office on the grounds that there is another post office not too far away and your post office is never very busy. However, your community believes that the post office plays a very important part in the area and has started a campaign to stop the closure of the post office.

(a) Write a letter to the Minister for Communications, Energy and Natural Resources objecting to the plan to close the post office. In your letter, include **THREE** arguments that you would make to convince the Minister that closing this post office would be a mistake. *(6 marks)*

(b) Design a poster that you would use to make local people aware of this issue. You should include a suitable campaign slogan with your drawing or picture. *(6 marks)*

(c) Describe **THREE** different peaceful activities, other than writing a letter to the Minister and designing a poster, that could be organised as part of the campaign. *(8 marks)*

Chapter 6 Democracy

Abraham Lincoln described democracy as 'government of the people, for the people, by the people'. When you study this concept, you will be looking at how we are governed in Ireland. You will get the chance to learn about the President of Ireland, the Taoiseach, the Tánaiste, the political parties and the other people who run the country. You will find out how laws are passed and discover just how our democratic government works.

One of the powers you have as a citizen is the power to vote. This right was won for you in the past, so when you are 18 years old, you will be responsible for casting your vote. So you'll know what to do when this time comes, studying democracy gives you the chance to learn all about voting and elections.

You may not be able to vote until you are 18, but you are still a citizen and so you already have a voice. In a democracy, there are many ways a citizen can get involved and take action, such as by lobbying a TD, writing to the people in power, getting involved in campaigns, petitions and the like.

You may already be involved in some democratic committees, like a school or Student Council or on a Green School committee or in Dáil na nÓg. These are some of the ways young people can experience democracy in action.

Flying the Flag

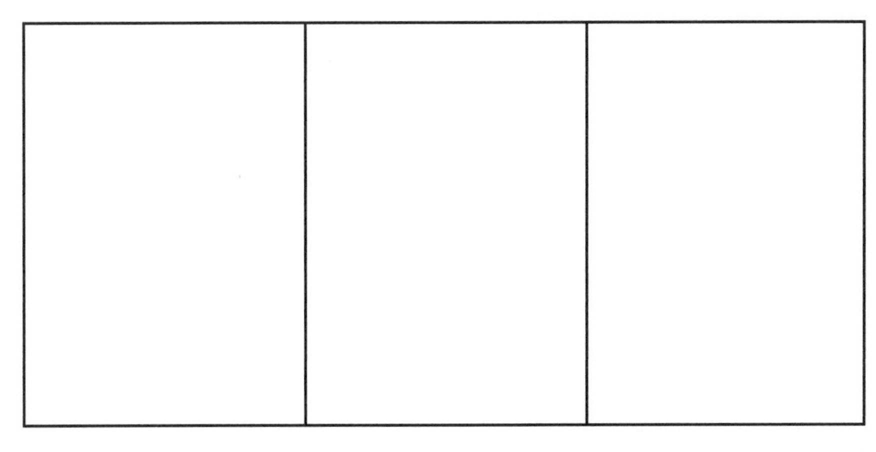

1. Colour in and describe the Irish flag and what it stands for.

2. When is the Irish flag flown at half-mast?

3. Why is the Irish flag sometimes placed on a coffin?

4. If the Irish flag flies beside another flag in Ireland, the Irish flag goes highest. Explain.

5. A country's flag is not meant to fly after dark. Why is this?

Who Represents YOU?

THE STATE IRELAND

PRESIDENT	TAOISEACH	TÁNAISTE
____________	____________	____________

THE OIREACHTAS

Local TDs

Name: ____________________

Party: ____________________

Name: ____________________

Party: ____________________

Name: ____________________

Party: ____________________

Name: ____________________

Party: ____________________

Name: ____________________

Party: ____________________

LOCAL GOVERNMENT

Have you a Mayor?

Name: ____________________

LOCAL COUNCILLORS

Name **THREE** of them.

Name: ____________________

Party: ____________________

Name: ____________________

Party: ____________________

Name: ____________________

Party: ____________________

Meet the Minister

Choose any government Minister and try to find out all the following information about him/her.

Draw or stick in his/her Department or party logo here.

Put photo of government Minister here.

The Minister I am going to study is: ______________________

1. The name of his/her Department is: ______________________
2. The address of his/her Department is: ______________________
3. His/her website is at: ______________________
4. **THREE** things this Minister is responsible for:
   (a) ______________________
   (b) ______________________
   (c) ______________________
5. This Minister represents the constituency of: ______________________
6. This Minister was first elected in: ______________________
7. This Minister belongs to the ______________________ Party.
8. The leader of this party is: ______________________
9. **TWO** issues that are important to this Minister are:
   (a) ______________________
   (b) ______________________
10. Would you vote for this Minister? ______________________
    Give a reason for your answer. ______________________
    ____

Who's Behind the Door?

Read the word or phrase on the door that describes the responsibility of the Department. Then write the name of the appropriate Minister below.

Hint: the names of all the Ministers are on the government website *www.gov.ie*.

4. Education and Skills

1. An Taoiseach

2. Finance

3. Foreign Affairs

10. Transport

5. Justice and Law Reform

11. Health and Children

6. Social Protection

12. Communications, Energy and Natural Resources

7. Community, Equality and Gaeltacht Affairs

13. Enterprise, Trade and Innovation

8. Tourism, Culture and Sport

14. Agriculture, Fisheries and Food

9. Defence

15. Environment, Heritage and Local Government

1. ____________________
2. ____________________
3. ____________________
4. ____________________
5. ____________________
6. ____________________
7. ____________________
8. ____________________
9. ____________________
10. ____________________
11. ____________________
12. ____________________
13. ____________________
14. ____________________
15. ____________________

Wanted for Public Office!

Take a look at the poster below, then fill in the posters for the other positions.

Q. Have you guessed who this poster is looking for?

A. ____

The Changing Role of Women in Politics

In a democracy all people are free to take part in government. For centuries women were expected not to take part in politics. They were expected to stay at home, do the housework and raise a family. Married women then were called 'housewives'. Things began to change in the 1960s and today women are working in business, government, education, medicine, the army. Now it is usual for both men and women to work outside the home and to share the housekeeping and family-rearing jobs.

What is your opinion of these changes? Write your thoughts below, then swap your answer with a classmate and compare your opinions.

My thoughts and opinions on the changing role of women are…

____

____

____

____

____

____

____

____

____

____

The Amazing Mrs Pritchard

When you have studied the poster above, answer the questions below in your copy.

1. (a) What is Mrs Pritchard's election poster slogan?
   (b) What political grouping does Mrs Pritchard represent? *(2 marks)*

2. (a) Why did Mrs Pritchard, a supermarket manager, decide to stand for election?
   (b) What TV company produced the series? *(2 marks)*

3. (a) Why do you think the people decided to elect Mrs Pritchard?
   (b) What was Mrs Pritchard's election motto? *(2 marks)*

4. (a) Suggest **TWO** reasons why young people are not interested in voting.
   (b) Describe **ONE** action **THE GOVERNMENT** could take to encourage young people to vote. *(4 marks)*

5. Imagine that you have been selected by a political party to contest the next general election. Apart from campaign leaflets and election posters, describe **TWO** other ways in which you could encourage the public to vote for **YOU**. *(4 marks)*

Who Needs a Government?

We have a government for many reasons: to make laws, to collect taxes, to make sure that Ireland's interests are protected, to develop the country, to have a voice in international affairs and so on.

Below is a list of 10 reasons why we have a government. Your task is to rank each reason, with 1 being the most important reason for having a government in your opinion and 10 being the least important reason. Explain your choice.

RANK	REASON	EXPLANATION
	to provide information for people	
	to keep the economy safe	
	to look after the welfare of citizens	
	to have a strong army	
	to protect religious freedom	
	to collect taxes	
	to pass good and fair laws	
	to protect people's rights	
	to protect Ireland's natural resources	
	to have a voice on the international stage	

Voting: For the Want of a...

For the want of a VOTE
A QUOTA was lost
For the want of a QUOTA
A SEAT was lost
For the want of a SEAT
A MAJORITY was lost
For the want of a MAJORITY
A PARTY was lost
For the want of a PARTY
A GOVERNMENT was lost...
And all for the want of a VOTE.

1. What is the message of this poem?

___

___

___

___

2. Why is it important to vote?

___

___

___

___

3. Explain the meaning of each word in capital letters above.
   (a) Vote ___
   (b) Quota ___
   (c) Seat ___
   (d) Majority ___
   (e) Party ___
   (f) Government ___

4. Think up a slogan that encourages young people to vote.

If You Could Vote Tomorrow: Asking the Right Questions

Imagine its election time and the local candidates are going to knock on your door. You want to ask the right questions when they do so that you can decide who you will vote for. Choose **THREE** issues you want to know about and write down **TWO** questions about each of them that you would like to ask the candidate.

First issue you are interested in ______________________

Questions you will ask:

1. ______________________
2. ______________________

Second issue you are interested in ______________________

Questions you will ask:

1. ______________________
2. ______________________

Third issue you are interested in ______________________

Questions you will ask:

1. ______________________
2. ______________________

CSPE Exam 2007, Section 2, Question 3

Voting at 16

Voting age must be lowered to give youth a real voice

Michael McLaughlin

Young people should be central to all decisions which affect them and their voices should be heard across the board as often as possible.

But will young people be able for such responsibility? Surely they will make stupid and ill-informed decisions? The same arguments were of course put about giving women the vote and extending the voting age to 18.

I had the pleasure of recently accompanying a group of young people to Geneva under the auspices of the Children's Rights Alliance to meet the United Nations Committee on the Rights of the Child. While escorting such a group naturally involved a bit of effort and time, the only occasion when I had no work to do was when the young people were speaking directly to the committee about their lives - after all who knew this story better than they did?

Involving young people in decisions should not just be limited to sensitive or controversial issues; the day-to-day issues are just as important. Education is an obvious area where student councils mark only the start of establishing young people as partners with teachers and parents. Public transport, policing, housing, taxation - why draw the line? A real say in society and full inclusion in decision-making will only come about with the extension of the franchise (voting age) to 16.

Michael McLaughlin is Director of Central Services with Youth Work Ireland and a board member of the Children's Rights Alliance.

Adapted from original article which appeared in The Irish Times on Monday 28th June 2006

When you have studied this newspaper article, answer the questions below in your copy.

(a) What argument is made against young people voting at 16?
Why were some Irish young people visiting Geneva? *(2 marks)*

(b) From the newspaper article, name the **TWO** organisations working with children and young people.
According to Michael McLoughlin, what will need to happen if young people are to have a real say in Irish society? *(3 marks)*

(c) Suggest **TWO** ways that you think society would gain from lowering the voting age to 16? *(2 marks)*

(d) Apart from lowering the voting age to 16, describe **TWO** actions **IRISH POLITICIANS** can take to involve young people more in politics. *(4 marks)*

(e) Imagine you have just been appointed by the Children's Rights Alliance to run a campaign to have the voting age lowered to sixteen. Write a slogan which you would use to encourage people to get involved in this campaign. *(3 marks)*

Democracy: Rights and Responsibilities

Have you ever heard someone say 'Get a life'? I bet you have. You know by now that you have a civic life too. Civic life is about the political rights and responsibilities you have as a citizen. Political rights are powers and privileges that all citizens have and political responsibilities are about the duties a citizen has which make a society a place that represents the people better.

Which of the statements below are rights and which are responsibilities?

1. To a fair trial in a court of law. ______________________
2. To have a vote. ______________________
3. To obey the law. ______________________
4. To protest. ______________________
5. To travel from one country to another. ______________________
6. To criticise the government. ______________________
7. To serve on a jury. ______________________
8. To use the right to vote. ______________________
9. To pay taxes. ______________________
10. To respect the rights of others. ______________________

The Public Agenda

An agenda is a list of things to be done. The public agenda is the list of issues that individual citizens in Ireland can take part in if they wish. Below is a diagram showing some issues or problems on the public agenda.

Tick the issues and the ways to take action that interest you.

ISSUES	Possible action							
	Write to the newspaper	Join an interest group	Make posters and hang them in key places	Visit your TD's clinic	Join a voluntary organisation	Go on a march	Start a postcard campaign	Write to your TD
Poverty								
Vandalism								
Free education								
Joy riding								
Health care								
Drug abuse								
Unemployment								
Put your own issue here ____________ ____________								

Democracy

1. Match the job title below with the work that the person holding this office does. You can use each title and office only once.

a. Taoiseach	**1.** Chairs the sessions of the Dáil and keeps order there.
b. Party Whip	**2.** Stands in for the Taoiseach when he is absent.
c. Tánaiste	**3.** Makes sure that all people in the political party know what way to vote.
d. Ceann Comhairle	**4.** Is elected to represent people in her/his constituency.
e. TD	**5.** Is the leader of the government.

2. Fill in the spaces in the sentences below. The first letter has been done for you.

(a) A TD who does not belong to any party is called an I ________________.

(b) When two or more parties come together to form a government this is called a C________________.

(c) The voting system used in Ireland is called P________________ R________________.

(d) Each year in December the Budget is presented by the Minister for F______________.

(e) There are o ________________ h ________________ and s________________ -s________________ TDs in the Dáil.

3. Tick the one correct answer in the boxes below.

To vote you must be on:	A person fighting for a seat in an election is called:
☐ **A** the Roll of Electors	☐ **A** a TD
☐ **B** the Register of Electors	☐ **B** a candidate
☐ **C** the List of Electors	☐ **C** an officer
Voting takes place in:	**The person who calls out the result of an election is called:**
☐ **A** a ballot station	☐ **A** The voting manager
☐ **B** a polling station	☐ **B** The returning officer
☐ **C** a voting station	☐ **C** The counter

Student Councils

Student councils are a democratic way in which some schools involve students in decision-making processes.

1. Which of the following benefits of Student Councils do you see as most valuable? Choose no more than **FIVE** and number them in order of priority, starting with 1 for most valuable, in the boxes on the right-hand side.

Improves student-teacher relationships in the school as a whole	
Teaches students about democracy	
Improves student attitudes to school	
Encourages students to take responsibility in the life of the school	
Gives students a chance to see and hear different viewpoints and values	
Helps students to develop and express their views	
Helps to develop students' listening and decision-making skills	
Provides new views for the school staff that help them manage the school more effectively	
Prepares students to take a more active role in society	

2. Explain why you selected these five.

____

____

____

____

____

3. What three pieces of advice would you give to a school thinking of setting up a Student Council?

(a) ______________________________

(b) ______________________________

(c) ______________________________

Vote for Me!

These students have decided to run for the Student Council as representatives for their class. Read their campaign speeches and decide which one you would vote for.

Tick the candidate you would vote for, then give reasons for your choice.

I am on the school Gaelic and soccer teams and I swim every day, rain or shine. I think we need to improve all the sports facilities in the school and if I'm elected, I will fight hard for this goal.

Lorcan

Everybody says I'm a very good listener and I will be good at listening to what the class wants. I believe in fairness and will fight hard for this. Fair treatment for all is the big issue.

Martin

My big campaign issue is bullying. I know we don't have much bullying in this school and I want to keep it that way. I would like to set up an anti-bullying committee and have an anti-bullying week.

Eoghan

I have won lots of drama prizes and I have got medals for making speeches. I will be the best person to represent the views of the class and at speaking out for your issues.

Úna

I think that clubs after school is a big problem in this school. I will fight to have more clubs where we can do art, cookery, chess and computers. There's nothing to do here after school and I want to change that.

Bríd

My opinion is that it is important that girls have equal opportunities on sports teams and other clubs in the school. I will make sure that girls get a fair share.

Anna

Reasons for my choice:

____

____

____

____

____

Themus Island Conflict

In a faraway corner of the world there is an island called **Themus**. There are two tribes of people there, **the Thems** who believe that the mountains are more important than the sea and another, **the Usses**, who believe that the sea is more important than the mountains.

Whenever these two groups meet there is trouble. They argue and fight over the sea and the mountains. These troubles have gone on for generations. At times, there has even been violence between the two groups. As a result of all the trouble, the two groups now live at opposite ends of the island. The adult Thems and Usses never spend time with each other and the only time the two sides meet is when they drop off their children at the one school on the island of **Themus**.

Everybody on **Themus** is fed up of all the trouble and want to end it. A special committee has been set up to offer some suggestions to **the Thems** and **the Usses**.

Look at the suggestions below and then rank the ten suggested solutions in order from 1 to 10 – 1 is the best solution and 10 is the worst. Explain your ranking in your copybook.

Build a second school and keep the two sides completely separate.	Bring in the army and force one side to agree with the other.
Put the **Usses** in prison if they say that the sea is better than the mountains. Put **the Thems** in prison if they say that the mountains are better than the sea.	Encourage **the Thems** and **the Usses** to respect the fact that not everyone believes the same thing. They could start learning this at school.
Bring the two sides together to see if they can agree on some things and begin again from there.	Arm the two sides so that they can have a proper war and end the troubles once and for all.
Banish all **the Usses** to another island.	Banish all **the Thems** to another island.
Get **the Thems** and **the Usses** to argue more so that they get fed up and stop.	Build a big wall and divide the island in two.

Can you think of other solutions?

Can you think of any real conflicts that are like the one on **Themus**?

Describe one of these conflicts.

Northern Ireland Murals

1. Draw in symbols and decorate this gable wall to represent views of the nationalist community.

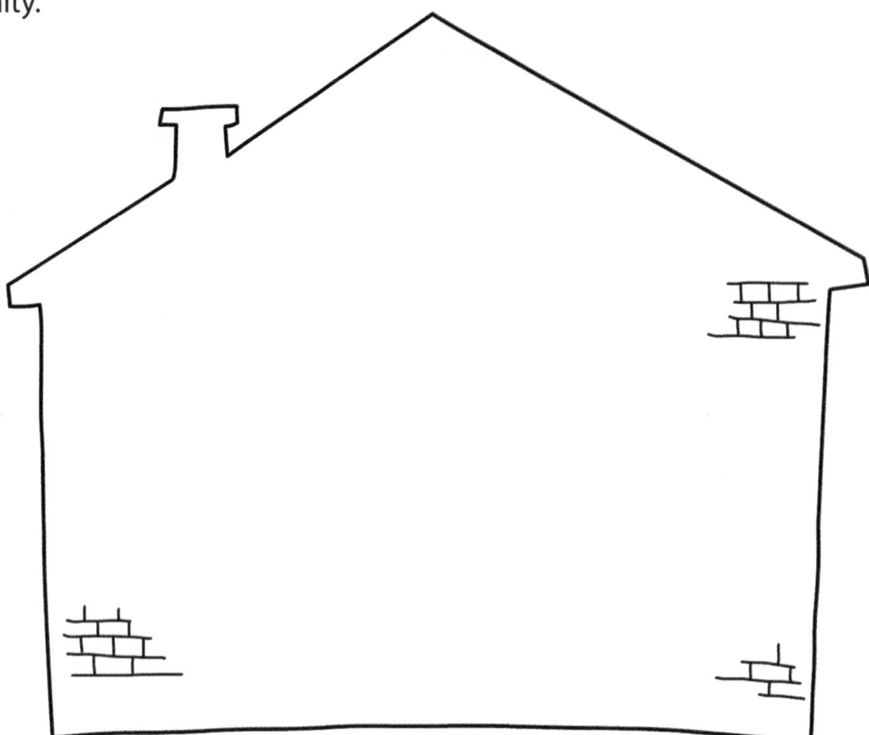

2. Draw in symbols and decorate this gable wall to represent views of the unionist community.

Section 3 Questions

1. Teaching Them a Lesson

Your CSPE class want to speak to the 6th class pupils in the local primary school about how important it is to vote when you are over 18.

(a) Write a letter to the Principal of the Primary school explaining why you want to talk to the 6th class pupils. Include **THREE** reasons why you think it is important for the 6th class students to hear you speak. *(6 marks)*

(b) Write out **FOUR** points you would include on a poster that you would bring to show the 6th class pupils. *(8 marks)*

(c) Describe **TWO** ways that would allow you to decide if this visit was a success or not. *(6 marks)*

2. A visit to Áras an Uachtaráin

Having studied the concept of democracy, imagine that your CSPE class has decided to invite Uachtarán na hÉireann (the President of Ireland) to talk to your class and to answer questions.

(a) Describe **THREE** issues which you would like to discuss with the President. *(6 marks)*

(b) On behalf of the class, write a letter of invitation to the President, explaining the purpose of the visit. *(8 marks)*

(c) Name and explain **THREE** benefits that might result from such a visit. *(6 marks)*

3. Election Campaign

In some countries the law requires citizens to vote at election time: if you don't vote you can be fined.

(a) Your class is interested in this practice and is holding a debate on it.

Write notes for speakers in the debate, giving **ONE** argument in favour of this practice and **ONE** argument against it. *(6 marks)*

(b) Barack Obama used text messages to encourage people to turn up to vote for him in the US presidential election. This was a successful strategy.

(i) In your opinion why was this successful?

(ii) Compose a text message that a politician could send out to encourage people to vote. Your message should use at least 160 characters (characters = letters, numbers and spaces). *(6 marks)*

(c) In 2009 only 43% of citizens, entitled to vote in the European election, turned out to do so. This was the lowest turnout ever in a European election.

Write to your local **MEP** suggesting **THREE** ways in which people could be encouraged to turn out to vote in European elections. *(8 marks)*

Chapter 7 Law

Overview of Law

Where would we be without laws? Laws are a very important part of our society. They help to keep order in the country, to protect life and property and they are a guide for people's behaviour. Laws are not a new invention – they have been with us in some shape or form for centuries.

In Ireland, laws are passed by the government after a very careful process. Laws are carried out by our police force, an Garda Síochána. We have a system of courts which deal with civil and criminal cases. There are prisons in different parts of the country where criminals serve time for their crimes if convicted and sentenced to prison. People are also fined, get suspended sentences, community service orders and penalty points as punishment for breaking the law.

The law affects all parts of our lives – labour laws that deal with working hours, consumer laws that deal with our rights as shoppers and traffic laws that deal with traffic offences like speeding.

The laws we have make our world a safer place.

It's the Law – True or False

Read each of the following statements and decide if they are true or false by circling the appropriate letter, then fill in the empty boxes with your own true/false statements about the law.

Hint: See Chapter 7 of your *Make a Difference!* textbook for ideas.

The highest court in Ireland is the High Court.
T F

The Small Claims Court can settle disputes up to €2000.
T F

All family law cases are held *in camera*, which means that they are not open to the public.
T F

There are two prisons in Mountjoy, one for men and one for women.
T F

There is always a jury in the Central Criminal Court.
T F

It is the duty of the court to pass laws.
T F

Women cannot become Supreme Court Judges.
T F

The Supreme Court sits in the High Court in Dublin.
T F

T F

T F

T F

T F

T F

T F

T F

T F

What if...? Laws

What if...? Law 1

What if a new law was passed that said young people do not have to attend school if they don't want to?

(a) List the advantages of this law for young people.

(b) List its disadvantages for young people.

(c) Do you think this would be a good law? Why or why not?

(d) If this law came into force, what would you do about your schooling?

What if...? Law 2

What if a new law was passed that said in order to become an adult, you have to pass a special exam?

(a) Do you think this law is a good idea? Why or why not?

(b) Do you think there would be problems enforcing it? Why or why not?

(c) What sort of adulthood skills do you think should be tested by the exam?

What if...? Law 3

Suggest a law that you would like to see passed.

Offences and Offenders

1. Make a list of crimes under each of the following headings.

Minor offences	Serious offences	Extremely serious offences

2. If you were a judge, what punishment would you consider suitable for the following crimes?

(a) Joyriding – a second offence

(b) Mugging – a third offence

(c) House-breaking – a first offence

(d) Shoplifting – a second offence

(e) Under-age drinking – a first offence

Law

1. Match the job title below with the type of work each person does in relation to the law. You can use each name and issue **only once**.

1. Barrister	a. arrests criminals
2. Garda	b. keeps a written record of what people say in court
3. Stenographer	c. is in charge of a prison
4. Judge	d. studies the law to help people to make a good case
5. Prison warden	e. makes decisions after hearing all the evidence

2. Fill in the gaps in the sentences below. The first letter in each word has been given to you.

(a) The court that decides on matters that relate to the Constitution is called the S__________ C__________.

(b) F__________ L__________ cases are heard *in camera*.

(c) If you cannot afford a solicitor or barrister then you can get F__________ L__________ A__________.

(d) The Minister for J__________ is in charge of the courts.

(e) There are usually t__________ people on a jury.

3. Tick the one correct answer below.

The court that travels around the country is called: ☐ **A** The Travelling Court ☐ **B** The Circuit Court ☐ **C** The District court	In the Small Claims Court the largest claim you can make is: ☐ **A** €500 ☐ **B** €2000 ☐ **C** €3000
The most judges you can have in the Supreme Court is: ☐ **A** 3 ☐ **B** 5 ☐ **C** 10	If you sue someone for damaging your property this is a: ☐ **A** a Criminal Case ☐ **B** a Civil Case ☐ **C** a Basket Case

The Garda Reserve

"I'm Declan. I'm 46 and I run my own business."

"My name is Louise. I'm 30 years old and I'm a teacher"

"My name is Lee. I am 24 years old and I'm a waiter."

"I'm Gerry. I'm 53 and recently retired."

"I'm Mary. I'm 23 and I'm a graduate."

Whoever you are and whatever you're doing, you may not have heard about the far-reaching changes taking place in An Garda Síochána. It is an exciting time to join Ireland's national police service - whether as a Garda Trainee or as one of the very first members of the new Garda Reserve.

Serving the public as a Garda or Garda Reserve Member requires the kind of professionalism that will help us achieve our goal of a safer Ireland for everyone. And these career opportunities are open to everyone.

Garda Trainee

You must be aged between 18 and 35 and meet minimum education and health requirements. Fluency in English or Irish required.

Garda Reserve

You must be aged between 18 and 60 and be willing to give 4 hours per week to the service of your community. Fluency in English or Irish required.

Information on all career opportunities with An Garda Síochána can be found at www.garda.ie

Applicants for Garda Trainee should apply at www.publicjobs.ie

Closing date for applications is 19 September 2006

Applicants for the Garda Reserve should apply at www.publicjobs.ie or phone LoCall 1890 261 000

FOR MORE INFORMATION, GO TO:
www.garda.ie

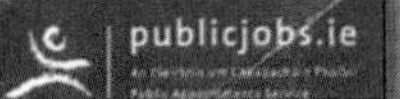

When you have studied the leaflet above answer the questions below in your copy.

1. According to the advertisement, what is the goal of the Garda and the Garda Reserve? *(1 mark)*

2. (a) What age must you be to become a trainee Garda?
   (b) What age must you be to become a member of the Garda Reserve?
   (c) How much time must you be willing to give in the service of your community to become a member of the Garda Reserve? *(3 marks)*

3. (a) Why do you think people must be fluent in Irish or English to join these forces?
   (b) Where does the advertisement say you can get more information on these forces? *(3 marks)*

4. Many European countries have a police reserve force. What is the purpose of these forces? *(3 marks)*

5. Describe **TWO** actions that **THE MINISTER FOR JUSTICE AND LAW REFORM** could take to encourage more people to join the Garda Reserve Force. *(4 marks)*

Crime and Punishment

Imagine it's 2060 and the law has changed in order to keep crime at a minimum.

- Now petty criminals wear a collar with a tiny tracking device so that the Gardaí always know where they are.
- Other criminals are branded on the forehead and people wearing a brand aren't allowed into certain places or to hold certain jobs.
- More criminals are deported and sent off to a space station, where they don't come into contact with other people until their sentence is served.
- Finally, really dangerous criminals are given brain transplants from good-living people who have died in traffic accidents.

1. What are the advantages and disadvantages of the four methods described above?

____

____

____

____

2. Which of the **FOUR** methods do you like best? Why?

____

____

3. Which of the **FOUR** methods do you think is unlikely to ever happen?

____

____

4. Describe another suitable punishment that could be used in the future.

____

____

____

The Crime Victims Helpline

Effects of Crime

If you are a victim of crime you may feel:

- Alone or isolated
- Anxious or depressed
- Afraid to go out
- Angry and let down

How do we help?

We are here to listen.

Our primary focus is on emotional support, providing the opportunity for you to talk about your experience in confidence.

We listen with empathy, and without judgement.

If you feel isolated, or do not know who to talk to, we are here to listen and to give you our time.

We can also help in liaising with the Gardai and other agencies and services.

We provide information on

- Local support services where available
- Services available for victims of particular crimes
- All aspects of the criminal justice system
- Rights and entitlements regarding compensation, legal aid, the courts

- a service funded by the Commission for the Support of Victims of Crime, and provided by volunteers.
www.crimevictimshelpline.ie **info@crimevictimshelpline.ie**

Read the brochure above and answer the questions below in your copy.

1. Name three effects of crime.
2. What is the email address of the organisation that produced this leaflet?
3. Who else does the leaflet say you can contact if you need to talk to someone?
4. List three things that this organisation provides.
5. Do you think that the victims of crime need support? Explain your answer.
6. There is no slogan on this leaflet. Compose a suitable slogan for this organisation.

Ballygosloe

Ballygosloe is a small town in Ireland, not too far from you. It has a terrible problem as many cars are speeding around the place. The speed limit is 50 kilometres per hour in the town and 80 kilometres an hour on the roads outside the town. Nearly everyone seems to ignore the speed limit.

The people who were caught speeding made excuses like:

The Road Safely Authority is worried by the number of crashes that have recently taken place in Ballygosloe and want to send a car sticker into every home for the back of cars to remind people to slow down. Your task is to design the car sticker.

Section 3 Questions

LAW SURVEY

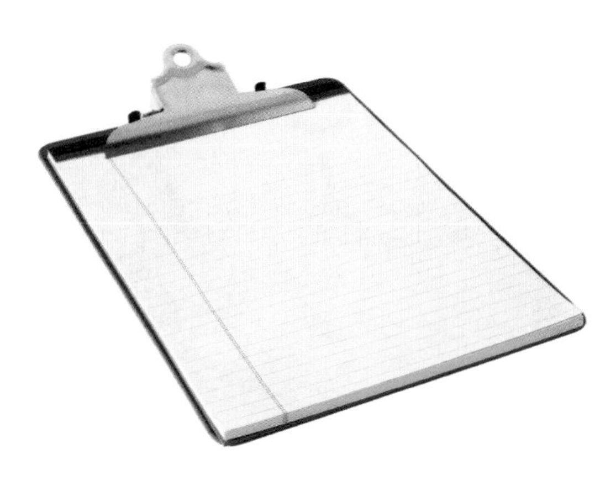

Your class want to carry out a survey as a way of finding out information and about peoples' attitudes. You have decided to investigate the law in Ireland.

(a) Name **THREE** areas of the law that you will focus on in the survey and explain why you have picked those areas. *(6 marks)*

(b) Write out **SIX** questions that you think would be important to include in your questionnaire and explain why you would ask EACH of them. *(6 marks)*

(c) Write a paragraph explaining what you would do with all the information that you collect. *(8 marks)*

CSPE Exam Paper 2009, Section 3, Question 4

CCTV (Closed Circuit Television)

Your local town is planning to install CCTV cameras as part of a campaign to reduce crime in your area. Your CSPE class is interested in this, and has asked your teacher if you can do an Action Project about this issue.

(a) Your class has decided to have a debate on the topic, 'CCTV Reduces Crime', before carrying out the Action Project.

Write down **ONE** argument in favour and **ONE** argument against this topic. *(6 marks)*

(b) Name **ONE** action that you could undertake to find out how students in your school feel about CCTV cameras. Name **TWO** committees that you would set up in order to carry out this action. After you have carried out this action, what would you do with your findings? *(8 marks)*

(c) Design a poster you would use to show students in your school how you feel about the CCTV cameras. As well as a drawing, your poster should include a **SLOGAN** which will show students your opinion on the use of CCTV cameras in your town. *(6 marks)*

Chapter 8 Interdependence

Overview of Interdependence

Interdependence is a way of describing the ways we are linked to other people and other countries around the world. If you think about the food you eat, the clothes you wear and the things you have, you will quickly realise just how you are connected to places far and wide. If you lived outside of Ireland, you might discover that there are ways in which people from other countries are connected to us too.

Once you realise all the connections you have around the world, you can think about the choices you make that influence people in far-away places, such as the clothes you buy that are made in sweatshops, the shoes you wear that are made by child labour, the coffee you drink or the bananas you eat for which the farmer gets very little. You have the choice to make a difference and to buy wisely (for example, buying Fairtrade products) in order to be a responsible citizen.

Interdependence is also about the organisations Ireland is linked to. In particular, Ireland is a member of the European Union and plays an important role there through our MEPs. We are also involved in the United Nations. The UN is based in New York and Ireland has representatives there. Ireland also sends troops on peacekeeping duty to countries the UN is involved with.

Ireland is a small island at the edge of Europe, but studying this concept allows you to explore the various ways that Ireland is linked in so many ways to places all over the globe.

From Seed to Slice

These pictures show how bread comes into being. Write out the story and highlight the different stages involved.

Hamburger Hassle

One weekend, a group of young people handed out leaflets outside a fast food restaurant. After some time, the manager of the restaurant came out and asked the young people to move off. The young people refused to move.

A Garda appeared on the scene and asked the group to move away from the entrance because they were causing an obstruction. The young people moved away but continued to hand out the leaflets. Here's one of the leaflets.

Stop & Think

Before you eat at this restaurant, you should know:

- This company buys millions of tonnes of beef every year from countries such as Brazil.
- To provide grazing land for the cattle, millions of acres of tropical rainforest have been destroyed.
- These forests were home for both people and animals. Both have been displaced by the bulldozer and the cattle herds.
- These forests are the lungs of our planet.

What can you do?

- Stop eating hamburgers made from beef.
- Try alternative non-meat snacks.
- Write to the company and tell them why you won't be eating at their restaurants any more. You have real spending power – money talks.
- Write to one of the embassies and make your protest about the destruction of the rainforests herds.

1. Do people have the right to hand out leaflets like this? Explain your answer.

____

____

2. What effect might each of the **FOUR** actions outlined in the leaflet have?

The Domino Effect

MultiWear Closure – A Body Blow to Midlands

The news, when it came from MultiWear, was as grim as expected: the midlands-based clothing company announced the closure of its factories at Ballysad, Ballybrounock and Dungrim. In all, some 560 jobs will be lost over the next three months.

In the end, these three towns could not escape the global trend in the clothing industry, which has seen all the big companies relocating to low-cost places like Morocco, the Caribbean and elsewhere. A switch to Morocco, where wages are only a fraction of the average €346 per week paid to workers in the midlands, has clear benefits for a company which has been suffering heavy losses.

The developments at MultiWear have led to demands for tighter control on multinationals that receive generous grant-aid and then relocate with little advance warning.

1. Why do you think MultiWear is closing its three factories in the midlands?

____

____

2. Many people will be affected by the closure. Rank them from 1 to 15 (1 for the most affected, finishing with 15 for those least affected). Explain how any four of them will be affected.

☐ The workers	☐ The accountant	☐ The factory owner
☐ The caterer	☐ The boutique owner	☐ The contract cleaner
☐ The shopper	☐ The haulage company	☐ The fashion designer
☐ The cotton picker	☐ The advertising agency	☐ The maintenance firm
☐ The thread supplier	☐ The button maker	☐ The landscape gardener

(a) ____

(b) ____

(c) ____

(d) ____

3. Make a list of the connections you think these factories may have had beyond the midlands – at national, European and global level.

____

____

____

____

You Choose...

When it comes to buying things, we all have choices to make. As with many choices, there are pros and cons. Think about the following issues that influence people when they buy food.

TYPE OF SHOPPING	CONS
ORGANIC Some people just want food that has no chemicals in it.	But…
COST Some people just buy the cheapest food they can get.	But…
LOCAL Some people just like to support their local shopkeeper.	But…
CONVENIENCE Some people just buy food wherever it is handy for them to shop.	But…
ENVIRONMENTAL Some people are very aware of the environment and buy food that has been grown locally and so hasn't travelled long distances causing pollution.	But…
FAIRTRADE Some people like knowing that the food they buy has been grown by people who get paid a fair price for their goods.	But…

Here is a list of cons. Put the correct letter in the column beside the issue connected to that form of shopping. You **CAN** use the same letter more than once.

(a) It costs a lot.

(b) It is not always convenient.

(c) Some places don't stock these goods.

(d) The food might not be organic.

(e) The food might not be fairly traded.

(f) The environment might have been damaged in producing these goods.

(g) The money made on selling these goods might not stay in the local area.

Can you think of any other **CONs**?

Fairtrade

When you have studied the leaflet above, answer the following questions in your copy.

1. (a) What does the Fairtrade mark guarantee?
   (b) What is the website address? *(2 marks)*

2. (a) Name **TWO** different Fairtrade foods that are now available.
   (b) Name **OTHER** non-food Fairtrade products that are now in our shops. *(3 marks)*

3. (a) What does the Fairtrade logo represent?
   (b) Suggest an alternative logo for Fairtrade. *(2 marks)*

4. Suggest **TWO** actions **YOUR CSPE CLASS** could take to encourage the school staff and students to buy Fairtrade products. *(4 marks)*

5. Decisions we make in Ireland can directly affect the lives of people living thousands of miles away. Describe **TWO** other ways in which our actions can directly affect people living far away. *(3 marks)*

The Council of Europe

"Look, sis, democracy is a system where people who live in a particular country are free to choose their own leaders. Human rights are the most important rights there are, like the right to think and say what you want."

"So human rights are for everyone!" said Sue.

"Of course they are!" replied Max. "To put it in a nutshell, the Council of Europe is a place where all the European peoples can meet to make sure we all live together in peace and friendship."

Sue nodded.

"That's great," she murmured, "but it can't always be easy. How do they go about it?"

Max cleared his throat.

When you have studied the extract above, answer the following questions in your copy.

1. (a) What flag forms the back of Max's chair?
   (b) Why is the Council of Europe important? *(2 marks)*
2. What does Max say happens in a 'democracy'? *(2 marks)*
3. (a) What are the most important rights?
   (b) Name **TWO** rights mentioned in the extract. *(3 marks)*
4. The Council of Europe consists of 47 member states. Give **TWO** reasons why you think many of the countries in Europe have joined this international organisation. *(3 marks)*
5. The Council of Europe is based in Strasbourg. Give **TWO** reasons why you think Strasbourg is a good location. *(4 marks)*

Important European Citizens

Place photographs of the **EIGHT** people who hold the important European positions mentioned in each of the boxes provided below.

1. The President of the European Commission
2. The European Commissioner nominated by Ireland
3. The President of the European Council
4. High Representative of the European Union for Foreign Affairs and Security Policy
5. The President of the European Parliament
6. An MEP representing the East Constituency
7. An MEP representing the South or North-west Constituency
8. An MEP representing the Dublin Constituency

The European Commissioner nominated by Ireland

Profile Sheet

Place a photograph of the European Commissioner nominated by Ireland here

Name: ____________________

Commission area of responsibility: ____________________

Former political party (if applicable): ____________________

Name **FIVE** priority areas being worked on by this Commissioner:

1. ____________________
2. ____________________
3. ____________________
4. ____________________
5. ____________________

List **TWO** interesting facts about this Commissioner:

1. ____________________
2. ____________________

Design a Set of European Stamps

Design a set of stamps to represent any 15 EU member states. Choose a landmark, famous person or a symbol closely associated with each country.

European Institutions

Here are **SIX** photographs of European Institutions. In the space provided below, write down the name of the building which matches each picture.

- The European Parliament, Strasbourg
- The European Commission Building, Brussels
- Council of the European Union Building, Brussels
- The European Central Bank, Frankfurt
- The Council of Europe Building, Strasbourg
- The European Court of Human Rights, Strasbourg

(a) ______________________________

(b) ______________________________

(c) ______________________________

(d) ______________________________

(e) ______________________________

(f) ______________________________

The European Union Explained

Imagine that you have made contact with a student in a school that has applied for membership of the European Union, and the students there want to find out what life is like in the EU.

Write a letter to a student in this country. In it, briefly explain the three main institutions of the EU: the Commission, Parliament and Council. Also explain how membership of the EU has affected life in Ireland.

Dear

Yours sincerely

The European Union

CSPE Exam 2007, Section 3, Question 3

Europe Day, 9th May

In 1985 the 9th of May was chosen by the EU as the date on which to celebrate Europe Day. Your CSPE class has decided to celebrate Europe Day as part of your learning about interdependence.

(a) Write a short speech for a school assembly explaining your Europe Day programme of celebration. You should include a description of **THREE** different activities which everyone can take part in so as to learn more about the European Union. *(6 marks)*

(b) Apart from making a speech at the school assembly, describe **TWO** ways in which your class could raise awareness about your Europe Day celebrations. *(6 marks)*

(c) Name and explain **TWO** skills that you and your classmates would use while raising awareness about your Europe Day celebrations. *(8 marks)*

New EU Member State

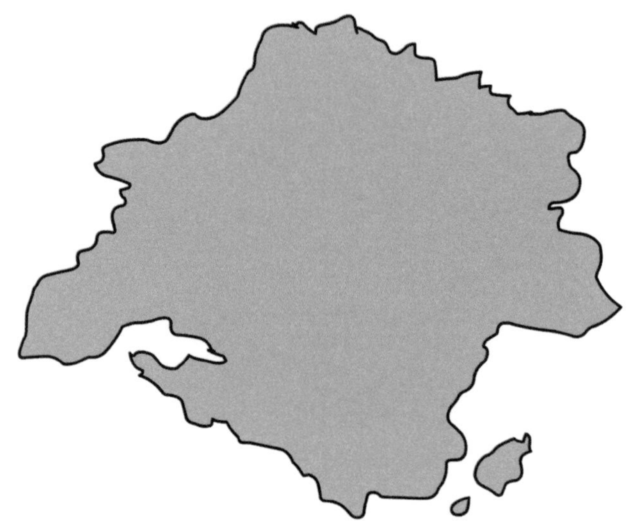

As the European Union (EU) continues to grow with new member states joining each year, your CSPE class has been invited by the local county council to take part in the celebrations to welcome the newest member. People from this new EU country will be travelling to your area to take part in the event.

(a) Write a speech to welcome the country, and in it include **THREE** benefits of belonging to the EU. *(6 marks)*

(b) Describe **THREE** activities, other than the welcome speech, that you could organise to mark this occasion. *(6 marks)*

(c) Choose **ONE** of these activities and describe the work of **THREE** committees that you would set up in order to organise it. *(8 marks)*

Snapshots of the United Nations

Here are **FOUR** photographs of United Nations Buildings. In the space provided, write down the name of the building which matches each picture.

- The International Court of Justice, The Hague (Netherlands)
- The United Nations Building, New York (USA)
- The United Nations Building, Geneva (Switzerland)
- The United Nations Security Council, New York (USA)

(a) ______________________

(b) ______________________

(c) ______________________

(d) ______________________

Place photographs in the spaces provided of **TWO** people working with the United Nations.

Ireland's Ambassador to the United Nations	United Nations Goodwill Ambassador

The United Nations Secretary-General

Profile Sheet

Place a photograph of the United Nations Secretary-General here

Name: ______________________________

Country of origin: ______________________________

Term of office: ______________________________

Name **FIVE** priority areas being worked on by the UN Secretary-General.

1. ______________________________
2. ______________________________
3. ______________________________
4. ______________________________
5. ______________________________

List **TWO** interesting facts about the UN Secretary-General.

1. ______________________________
2. ______________________________

Ireland and The United Nations

Corporal Georgina Kane in the Lebanon

I went to the Lebanon as a member of the Military Police in 1997. I spent some time in the famous Irish post, Camp Shamrock, Tebnine, South Lebanon. It was an excellent experience but equally it was a humanising one, in that you met the civilian people in the Lebanon and you really appreciated the importance of your soldiering. Many of these people would have had even more difficult lives had it not been for the work of the Irish peacekeeping forces.

Militarily, my time in the Lebanon gave me an opportunity to apply all the training that I had learned at the Curragh Training Camp in Kildare. Army life involves a lot of training, but other than working in border areas along Northern Ireland, the Lebanon is the only contact with direct action. Working in the Lebanon gives a polish to your military training. I have also served with NATO in Sarajevo, but I found the Lebanon to be much more dangerous.

Today, my most prized possessions are the two medals I received at Camp Shamrock, Tebnine, Lebanon.

Source: *Irish Independent*

Read Corporal Georgina Kane's account of duty in Lebanon above and answer the following questions.

1. Where did Corporal Kane spend her time in Lebanon?

 ____

2. Why was spending time in Lebanon so important to Corporal Kane?

 ____

 ____

3. Corporal Kane has also served abroad with NATO – in what city?

 ____

4. What are the **FOUR** purposes of the UN as set out in the UN Charter?

 (a) ____________________________________

 (b) ____________________________________

 (c) ____________________________________

 (d) ____________________________________

5. In the diagram below, fill in the names of the **SIX** main parts of the UN.

The United Nations High Commissioner for Human Rights

Profile Sheet

Place a photograph of the United Nations High Commissioner for Human Rights here

Name: ______________________________

Country of origin: ______________________________

Term of office: ______________________________

Name **FIVE** priority areas being worked on by the UN High Commissioner for Human Rights.

1. ______________________________
2. ______________________________
3. ______________________________
4. ______________________________
5. ______________________________

List **TWO** interesting facts about the High Commissioner.

1. ______________________________
2. ______________________________

Section 3 Questions

War and Peace

When you have studied the images above, answer the following questions in your copy.

1. (a) What is this image saying?
   (b) When Irish soldiers work with the UN, what is their role?
   (c) What does the dove represent? *(3 marks)*

2. (a) The photograph shows Irish soldiers on United Nations duty. What is the role of Irish soldiers when they are working with the United Nations?
   (b) Name **TWO** countries where Irish soldiers have served with the United Nations. *(2 marks)*

3. Mary Robinson was the United Nations High Commissioner for Human Rights for five years. What international document was she always trying to promote? *(2 marks)*

4. (a) Describe the United Nations flag.
   (b) Suggest **ONE** alternative design for the UN flag. *(3 marks)*

5. Suggest **TWO** activities **YOUR CSPE CLASS** could organise on United Nations Day, 24th October, to inform other students about the work of the United Nations. *(4 marks)*

Adapted from CSPE Exam 2006, Section 3, Question 4

Ireland's Membership of the United Nations

Since 1958, Ireland has played an important role in the peacekeeping work of the United Nations. In fact, the Irish Defence Forces are the seventh largest contributors of troops to the UN! Irish soldiers have served in many of the world's most troubled spots. Your CSPE class has decided to produce a booklet to celebrate Ireland's involvement in the UN.

(a) Design a cover for the celebratory booklet of Ireland's involvement in the United Nations. You should include a suitable title and a drawing or picture in your cover design. *(6 marks)*

(b) Write a speech you would make at the launch of the booklet, giving **THREE** reasons why you think the United Nations is important today. *(6 marks)*

(c) Apart from the celebratory booklet, describe **TWO OTHER** actions your CSPE class could take to celebrate Ireland's involvement in the United Nations. *(8 marks)*

Guide to Assessment in CSPE

9

We are almost at the end of the CSPE course, so this is your final reminder about assessment and examinations. By now you know that 60 per cent of the marks for your course will go for the Report on an Action Project (RAP) or the Coursework Assessment Booklet (CWAB) that you will submit the May before your Junior Certificate examination. You should have given it a lot of attention because it is very important. All through the textbook there are ideas for doing Action Projects and we hope you found one that you really enjoyed doing. We have also given you lots of advice and guidance in Chapter 10 of the textbook to help you to write up this part of the examination properly so that you can do well.

So that just leaves the 40 per cent of the marks that are awarded for your written paper answers. This workbook has many practice questions, so you should be familiar by now with the types of questions you will face in the exam. On the next page are a few final tips.

Finally, when you have the Junior Certificate exam completed, all that's left is for you to go *MAD – Make a Difference!*

Surviving the CSPE Exam

Sort these tips into the three categories below.

1. Be careful that you don't skip or miss any questions or pages in the exam booklet.

2. Take your time and reread your answers. Check that they all make sense. Add in anything that you remember at the last minute.

3. Read all the questions in the section before you start to answer any questions, especially in Section 3.

4. In Section 2, study the stimulus very carefully because a lot of the answers will be easily found there.

5. Always read the instructions carefully, for example how many questions you have to do in each section. Note, too, that some questions have a particular slant and you must answer the exact question you are being asked.

6. On the day of the CSPE exam, keep calm. Don't 'wind up' your friends by saying that you're nervous and are afraid of going blank and forgetting everything.

7. Don't leave revision until the last minute.

8. Do some old CSPE exam papers and practise the type of answers that the paper is looking for.

9. Make sure that all your answers come from the point of view of human rights, social responsibilities, respect and tolerance.

10. When you are revising, use the self-test at the end of every chapter in the textbook and ask someone else to check your answers.

11. Watch the clock and don't spend too long on any question.

12. Have a list of different types of actions learned off so that you will have plenty of ideas to choose from for the ACTION questions on the paper.

Before the CSPE exam	During the CSPE exam	When the CSPE exam is nearly over

Notes

Notes

Notes

Notes